*Aunt Jane McPhipps*

*And*

*Her Baby Blue Chips*

# Aunt Jane McPhipps

## And

## Her Baby Blue Chips

### by Frances V. Rummell

Prentice-Hall, Inc.
Englewood Cliffs, N. J.

*Any relation between Aunt Jane and her friends to persons investing in the stock market today is pure coincidence, and any actions suggesting real life predicaments have been created solely for the reader's edification.*

*Aunt Jane's opinions, however, which become firmly biased, are not happenstance, but reflect the author's conviction that investing for ladies may carry peculiar hazards but also most rewarding pleasures.*

To those valiant and ubiquitous lady amateurs—some seven million in all—who now invest in common stocks.
And especially to Ruth Morgan, who does her homework.

*Aunt Jane McPhipps*

*And*

*Her Baby Blue Chips*

Vasiliu

# *ONE*

~~~~~~~~~~~~~~~~~~~~~~~~~~~~~~~~~~~~~~~~~~

Her black sailor askew, her tear-streaked face needing powder, Jane McPhipps leaned forward in the front seat of Al Bonelli's old brown Volkswagen as if to help it climb San Francisco's steep California Street hill. The weather, cleansed by a morning fog, boasted a high sparkle, and the buff-colored apartment houses were smiling in the sunshine. But Jane didn't notice. For, together with her young neighbors, she was returning home from the funeral of her husband, Horace McPhipps, and all she could see was the hill ahead—with both widowhood and middle-age awaiting her on the other side.

Digging her heels into the floor board, holding closer to her armload of gladiolas, given her by the chapel attendant, Jane steeled herself against more tears, and then reached over to pat Al's arm. She must not think only of herself; Al, too, had loved Horace.

Where, she wanted to ask, does courage come from? Is courage a muscle that can be strengthened by exercise? Maybe the only way to have courage was to use it.

Trying it out, she told Al, "I have absolutely determined something. I'm going into my apartment alone." Her tone didn't come out as firmly as she'd intended. Trying again, she turned to Rosemarie and Eleanor in the back seat and warned, "Don't anybody try to argue with me." Rosemarie Bonelli was Al's wife, and Eleanor was the pretty little kindergarten teacher who lived down the hall.

1

This time Jane was so convincing that Rosemarie reproached her. "We've taken the whole afternoon off to be with you!" Rosemarie clerked in silver at Gump's.

Al turned to look at Jane. Her handsome face was pale. Still, he caught that stubborn glint in her blue eyes, which were narrowed with resolution—the way one looks during big decisions—and it made him swear roundly under his breath.

"Now, Aunt Jane," he said brusquely, "don't be any more stubborn than you have to be. Of course we're staying with you. It's all settled." A onetime pupil of Jane's in Galileo High, Al felt very protective, very filial. Besides, Rosemarie was Horace's niece, and Al had strong family feelings.

Jane could always tell when Al was annoyed with her. Then, and no other time, he called her "Aunt Jane"—as if the kinship gave him the right to authority.

"You're a dear," she finally said, softening a little. Al and Horace had been close, closer than Rosemarie and Horace—which was natural enough. "But the answer is No. I *must* try it alone."

Al lighted a cigarette and inwardly shuddered to think of the bind Jane was in. Al was a junior executive in the Bank of America, and he was perfectly well aware that Horace had departed this earth about as free of assets as when he had entered—that is, save for some musty bookkeeping manuals, old flute scores, a spare set of false teeth, a Masonic ring, Social Security, and enough life insurance to cover his widow for about two years of genteel poverty.

Turning to Jane, Al said kindly, "We've got figuring to do."

"But, why, dear," she asked, "are you worried?" The one thing that concerned Jane least was the idea of earning her own living again.

"You spend a few days on the small loan desk at a bank," he replied. And instantly he was sorry he'd said this. After all, not many people saw, as he did, the soft underbelly of people's personal finances.

As if reading Jane's thoughts, Eleanor now exclaimed, "Look, Jane, you can always go back to full-time teaching."

Jane gratefully replied, "Yes, thank God." For several years, doing substitute work in the schools, she had lived on the ready, like a fireman. It would seem strange to have a regular job again.

Turning into Bush Street, Al stopped the car in front of a greystone apartment building. Everybody got out, climbed a flight of stairs, and paused stolidly in front of Jane's door, as though to go in.

Pulling off her hat, Jane smoothed her soft black hair, which she wore in a smart French roll, her forehead fringed with the wispiest shadow bangs. Bracing her tired shoulders against the door frame, she said feelingly, "You're all sweet. But I've *got* to try it alone."

Al said, "Dammit, Aunt Jane. You're being impossible!"

Rosemarie asked anxiously, "Will you promise to bang on the kitchen wall if you want anything?"

Jane nodded. Their kitchens adjoined, and the wall between served as a primitive telegraph whenever they needed each other.

"I'll see you tomorrow." Jane pressed her hand on the worn brass knob. Then she turned her flushed face back toward her friends; as her courage faltered, she sounded like a debater worrying a detail to forestall the main issue. "There is one thing I can't take, you know. It's the word 'widow.' People begin thinking you're helpless! Now don't *you* begin that!"

"You would"—Al was smiling with the liquid brown eyes of the Southern Italian—"think of things like that." He reached around the flowers, hugged her, and then, having capitulated, hurried down the hall to his own door. Indecisively, Rosemarie and then Eleanor embraced Jane and tagged along after Al.

Only an hour before, they had seen Jane become difficult in a way that had struck the girls as disconcerting, but Al as rather comical. Yet the gesture she had made had driven straight through his heart. Determined to stay with her friends, Jane had shocked everybody by riding from the chapel to the cemetery in his old Volkswagen—which, in a line of rented black Cadillacs filled with members of Horace's Chess Club and fellow Masons, was not at all suitable for a bereaved widow. But what Al had loved was seeing how her defiance had got under the skin of Mr. Gresham.

As Horace's employer, old Gresham had been the self-appointed grand marshal of the cortege, and tearing up and down the line of cars looking for Jane, he'd found her at the tail end.

"Jane! You belong up front, in the Cadillac limousine!" Gresham had exclaimed. "This"—his gesture had specifically included Al's Volkswagen—"this isn't even dignified!"

Jane had barely been able to answer him. Then, when she had, all she'd said was, "Horace always hated pretense." Which had not been exactly the thing to say. And she had not budged.

Gresham had stomped off, waving the black-suited chief mortician the old cavalry sign for "Advance!", and climbed into a four-hole Buick. At the cemetery, from under his black Homburg, he had viewed Jane's party like an uncle disclaiming poor relations. Nobody really cared about that, for nobody liked Mr. Gresham anyway—he was too stingy, too much the manager. Nevertheless, Al had reflected at the time, the gentle relict of Horace McPhipps had already become somewhat unpredictable. Widowhood, apparently, was putting an edge on Jane's natural independence.

Resolutely turning her back on her friends, Jane opened her door on the familiar scene in which—the feeling rushed over her—it was now up to her alone to keep life moving along with purpose. The furniture she saw with a new eye—tables and chairs old-fashioned enough in the afternoon sun to stand out sharply in all their shabbiness. The little table by the side of Horace's old leather chair still held his pipe rack with his fourteen pipes, and against the chair still leaned the board Horace had used for studying chess problems and replaying, with her, the games of the masters.

Jane had loved Horace dearly and deeply. A gentle, quiet little man, he had for years been Gresham's head bookkeeper, and one of Jane's most poignant memories was of poor Horace's concern that he couldn't die economically but had to dissipate his widow's substance by stretching out the hideous expense of a coronary.

She had always scoffed at Horace's worry. She would simply go back to regular teaching. And now, with a sharp sense of compassion, she thought of young widows left with small children— how utterly terrifying that must be! She and Horace had never had children. Neither knew why nor tried to find out. They had never made separate, secret trips to the doctor in order to fix the blame. It just had not happened, and they had accepted their childlessness wistfully, and grown closer to each other.

Still standing with her armload of flowers in the middle of the room, not knowing which way to turn as she ached in her aloneness—still hearing Horace's voice and still seeing Horace's concerned and gentle face—Jane's eyes were finally drawn to a familiar motion. Kim, her Siamese cat, who was curled up beneath Horace's chair, seemed suddenly to understand her need for solace. Getting up with unusual purpose, Kim fetched his yarn ball from underneath a table and then began tossing it in the air, retrieving it, and then tossing it again. Jane suddenly burst into tears.

It was only an hour later that Jane reached out toward the only security she knew—teaching. She had taught for some years, had quit, and then had gone back as a substitute, which meant pocket money. But now, feeling the urgent need for action, she picked up her telephone and dialed a familiar number, the Board of Education. Speaking with an assistant superintendent she knew, she said confidently, "I guess at this time I'm ready for a full-time post." It seemed hardly necessary to explain to the good man that she would also need to eat for years to come.

But he dealt her a blow that made her heart flop and then stand still. "It may seem preposterous, Jane," he said, not unkindly, "but no one over forty is eligible for new full-time employment. But we'll be glad to keep you on our substitute list." Jane, who was forty-nine and whose fine skin made her look young enough to model swimming suits, was left quivering in a bog of helplessness. No matter how sympathetic the man's voice, what he had said had one meaning. There was no one, now, who really needed and wanted her. Except on a purely emergency basis. In her sudden panic at rejection, her thoughts flew to a story that had upset her as a child: the heroine, buried while still alive, could speak, but nobody could hear her.

Yet a feeling of helplessness did not remain easily with Jane. Somewhere within the inner woman lay the spirit of little David with a slingshot, and the only thing to do now was to marshal one's facts, size up one's opponent, stack one's ammunition, and take careful aim.

Rushing to check the schools' idiocy against the world's at large, she reached for her *San Francisco Chronicle,* quickly riffled through the Help Wanted ads and read again and again, "Applications invited, ages 18 to 35." A few hardy nonconformists went as high as 45. Only dimly, then, did Jane begin to sense that all this razzle-dazzle emphasis on youth was nothing new, but only new to her.

Jumping up from her chair, she ran into the kitchen and began beating with both fists upon the kitchen wall adjoining Al's and Rosemarie's apartment. Before she had returned to the living room, Al burst in like a man ready to put out a fire, and tall blond

Rosemarie, in blue jeans and with a beer can in hand, flew in right behind him, her big eyes widened with alarm.

"Did you know," Jane cried indignantly, "that I'm too old to get a regular job teaching? Or filing? Or selling geraniums? Or taking tickets at a laundromat?"

"What the hell?" said Al.

"Didn't you know?" she fairly stormed. "I'm supposed to sit in a corner in a shoulder shawl!"

Now Al and Rosemarie looked at each other and grinned. The picture of Jane in a shoulder shawl did not come through, but they obviously loved her coming to life again.

At that moment the telephone rang, and it could not have picked a better time. Or carried a more astonishing message. It was Mr. Gresham. Horace had been his head bookkeeper for thirty-five years, and Mr. Gresham had called only once before, years ago, when the draft board had pulled Horace's number. Since nothing less than catastrophe merited Mr. Gresham's attention, Al and Rosemarie were as startled as Jane, who seemed to listen forever. Then finally they heard her say, "Yes—yes, I do understand," but she looked utterly mystified. She went on, "Let me repeat what you said, to make sure. I am to take Horace's life insurance in a lump sum and send you $3,000 of it." Making excited faces at her friends and utterly confusing them, Jane said, in a voice strangely vibrant with warmth, "Mr. Gresham, you are a very, very generous man."

Placing the phone in the cradle, she stared then at the floor like a woman in a trance. But a deep breath restored her and she looked up as though surprised to see Al and Rosemarie still there. "Isn't Longfellow Leasing a lovely name?" she asked, happily. "Especially for a teacher of American Literature?" Suddenly taking the stance of an old-time elocutionist, she began reciting.

"Under the spreading chestnut tree the village
smithy stands,
A great and mighty man is he . . ."

"Come off it," Al demanded. He was not amused. "You trying to tell me that old skinflint is a great and mighty man? What does he want with your $3,000?"

With exasperating airiness, Jane explained, "Mr. Gresham just said, 'Jane, I *want* to do something for you. This is a sure thing.' And so he is buying me one hundred shares of a very nice stock."

"Stock! Oh, my God!" Al had begun to sputter. "That you would fall for Gresham. The old boy is rooking you, sure as hell. I never saw anything more crass." Terribly worked up, Al groaned, "Or more pitiable."

Jane's voice rose. "He said it would double!"

"Yeah," said Al. "I've heard that one before." Looking grey around the edges, he added, "I swear if there's anything sadder than a poor widow, it's a dumb widow."

"Do not," Jane rebuked him, "use that word!"

"But why," asked Rosemarie, siding with Al, "would Mr. Gresham be so generous all of a sudden? He never gave Uncle Horace any fringe benefits. Never even raised his salary the last five years."

Jane shrugged her shoulders, had no ready answer. Then, brightly, one came to her. "This kind of generosity doesn't cost him anything," she said, and persuaded by her insight, she said precisely the same thing again.

Al was not impressed. "Aunt Jane, you cannot do this. Gresham is a cold-hearted bastard. But suppose he weren't. I still wouldn't trust the stock market. I once knew a man . . ."

Jane interrupted. "Mr. Gresham may be what you call him," she conceded. "But Horace always said—and goodness knows he should have known—Mr. Gresham was as honest as any business man could afford to be."

"Al's father," said Rosemarie cheerfully, "lost his shirt in the market. And remember Uncle Jud in St. Louis. He jumped off Eads Bridge in '29. Right into the river and drowned."

"But that was the poor man's objective!" observed Jane, feeling unexpectedly humorous.

Al said coldly, "Back in '29 people just lined up to jump off Golden Gate Bridge. They just queued up."

"There wasn't any Golden Gate Bridge in '29!" Jane was triumphant.

Grinning sheepishly, Al hung on. "What I really want to know," he said, "is what Gresham means to get out of this. Besides your $3,000." He glowered. "That's a hell of a thing to do to a widow."

Jane flashed him a warning look. "That word is so—well, it's sort of biological."

For the next few months, thanks to San Francisco's mild winter, practically the whole city remained pink with health, and Jane received fewer calls than usual for substitute teaching. And while she couldn't really *wish* more teachers ill, she did go so far as to tell Eleanor, "I do hope more teachers marry and have more babies—with long maternity leaves. Seems to me our teachers are slipping." But the city's guardians of American Literature remained both a sturdy and celibate lot, and not destined to accommodate Jane's livelihood.

Consequently, during the rare times she did fill in, she began telling fellow teachers about her new magazine subscription service. She didn't have any such service yet, to be sure; but what was there to it besides getting some orders? Jane got out Horace's ancient L. C. Smith, typed out two hundred announcements of her new subscription service, and began distributing them in earnest. Saving on bus fare, she spent days walking up one side of Bush Street and down the other, then fanning out and walking up and down the Jones, Mason and Taylor Street hills—all the while leaving her announcements in people's mailboxes in order not to disturb them. Her handiwork looked so businesslike and thoughtful it made her heart soar, and she was especially pleased with her inspirational touch; "Subscribers calling from outside the Bay Area, please call collect." And Jane began rushing home from her rounds to take all the telephone calls.

None came.

By late winter Al was instrumental in getting her a temporary job serving as a telephone investigator for the Better Business Bureau. For asking certain shady dealers innocent-sounding questions about their prices on namebrand tools and cutlery, Jane was to receive $1.50 an hour plus expenses. This sounded promising—especially the expense account part.

"You are," Al grinned, "a big operator, a wheeler-dealer."

As it turned out, however, the calls required minutes, not hours, and since Jane used her own telephone the expense account part fizzled utterly. Worst of all, the Bureau's war on under-priced hardware was over in ten days. All Jane netted was $4.50 and a nice compliment on her telephone voice.

"Don't you feel bad," she bravely told Al. "I didn't want to week-end in Mexico this winter anyway."

A little later, through Rosemarie's influence, she took a brief pinchhitting job at Gump's, polishing silver in a back room. Jane might have rubbed the beautiful silver harder had she known what Mr. Gresham was up to with her dollars. But, wholly ignorant of the stock market, she did not even know how or what to wonder about it, and consequently she dismissed the whole prospect to a sort of wordless cold storage. Once in a while, whenever she felt hope rising, Al would quash it by worrying.

"I just hope," he once said outright, "you can get your three thousand back."

"Starving wouldn't hurt me any," Jane loftily replied. She usually weighed between 125 and 130 pounds, which, for a woman of five feet four in her heels, was not exactly underweight —but below 125 she could not get.

Stubbornly preaching the virtues of a saving account, Al scouted around until he found a bank paying $3\frac{1}{2}$ per cent instead of the 3 that his own bank paid, and with high optimism he even told Jane she could double her money, at that rate, in about 25 years. But Jane's hair was already greying a bit here and there—especially at the temples—and she couldn't be persuaded that doubling her money over the next quarter of a century would matter much one way or the other. Still, Al's concern touched her deeply, especially since he had so little money himself.

But about the savings account, she finally had to be firm. "I haven't the time!" she said. "It's the brassbound ring or nothing."

It was six months and three weeks from the day of Horace's funeral when Mr. Gresham called Jane again. She was sitting reading Help Wanted ads at the time, with Kim in her lap. Mr. Gresham didn't ask how she was making out. He didn't waste any words at all, but got straight to the point.

"I'm taking your profits," he said, "and mailing you a check." Only upon replacing the receiver did she grasp the significance of what he had said. Yes, he *had* said 'nine thousand dollars'. He had even said 'nine thousand one hundred dollars and a few cents'. She had blindly written the figures on the telephone pad before her.

Jane was a full minute collecting herself. But yes, Yes! He had said . . .

Stifling with excitement, she began squealing, but didn't hear it, clapped her hands but didn't know it. She ran around picking up Kim a dozen times, and a dozen times she set him down again. Kim finally growled.

Eventually, calming somewhat, she walked with firm deliberation to her highest kitchen cabinet, reached for her bottle of sherry, and cracked it open. It was now March, and since Christmas Jane had saved this bottle for a birthday or a wedding, whichever came first. She poured herself a teacup full, sat on her kitchen stool and glowed. Finally, on the back of an old shopping list, she figured her profits, less commissions. She had cleared $6,109.33!

She looked at the clock. It would be two hours before Al and Rosemarie and Eleanor would be home to hear the news. Finishing her sherry—and deciding she'd never make a solitary drinker—she hastily changed her dress to a suit, left the apartment, and hailed a cab.

"To Saks Fifth Avenue," she said—as if cabs were her way of life—and sat back to revel in the vistas of San Francisco.

Her heart thrilled to her beautiful city as she looked down past the trim apartment houses with their gleaming mailboxes, down past the clean vertical canyon that swept ahead—straight as a gun barrel—to the shimmering silver of the Bay Bridge. The sight of a bridge tower, rising with solemn strength, seemed suddenly to symbolize eternity. Happily, Jane reflected, but of course! All roads lead to Rome, and all bridges lead to San Francisco. Then came the exalted thought—with money, she could build a bridge to the whole magnificent world.

The taxi turned abruptly from Bush Street into Grant Avenue and Jane recalled her destination barely in time to check the meter and fish deep in her worn bag for change.

She knew exactly what she wanted at Saks Fifth Avenue. For years she had bought her shoes at a self-help outlet store, where brand names were erased and unsold styles a year or so old went for a song. Now, her eyes sparkling, she entered Sak's Italian Shoe Salon, where an accented gentleman with the manner of a Swiss banker moved her to a tapestried chair.

Jane paid too much for high-heeled pumps from Florence and then floated up Geary Street and paid too much at I. Magnin's for a hat with blue roses. Topping off everything next door at Blum's, she indulged in a mocha and raspberry Dreamboat. The pumps adorned her shapely ankles, the hat matched her blue eyes, and if the Dreamboat added a few ounces to her contours, this was no day to think about consequences.

She further astonished herself by invading the St. Francis' lobby where she tipped a bellhop a dollar for throwing away a cumbersome package. It contained her black walking shoes. Symbolically, for the moment at least, Jane's feet had left the ground. She had already staked her claim over the rainbow and its pot of gold was dazzling.

That evening when Al and Rosemarie got home—Eleanor was always being detained by faculty meetings—Jane had chilled martinis waiting, and her sense of theater was heightening by the moment. Inviting them in, she waved them grandly to their chairs and offered the martinis, which in themselves signalled a thrilling departure.

"Who," grinned Al, "gave you a bottle of gin?"

"You'd never guess!" Jane replied. Then she showed them her hat, and held up a strikingly handsome foot for their appraisal.

"Those pumps," Rosemarie said accusingly, "did not come from any outlet house." Suddenly remembering where she had seen them—she passed Saks Fifth Avenue on her way to lunch everyday—she screamed, "My God! Italian!"

"Right!" said Jane, proud of her.

She tried to tell them about Longfellow Leasing, but Al wouldn't believe her. He simply denied the whole thing. He finished his second martini before he said another word.

"Jane," he then began sententiously, "if what you're telling us is the truth, and I can't doubt it, because you're no liar and God knows that Gresham jerk is no joker, then let this be a lesson to you."

"Of course, Al! What lesson?"

"Quit when you're ahead. Never touch the market again."

Jane looked thunderstruck. "You mean rein in your horse at the goal post? Not me."

A second look at Jane's radiant face finally broke Al's resistance. That and the confident lift to her chin—even though the Lord only knew exactly what this would portend.

Jane cued him in. "To think this kind of thing has been going on—and nobody told me!"

"Such beginner's luck shouldn't happen to a dog," Al went on sadly. "Gives you phony ideas."

"Al!" chided Rosemarie. "Quit moping. Get happy. Jane's done it!"

From this point on, considering everything, it took only a brief time for Jane to be convinced that what had happened once was bound to happen again. Finally, with martinis improving his outlook, even Al began to join in.

"Gresham just acted out of a guilty conscience," he argued. "He's not so bright. Anybody could do the same thing."

"Jane could!" said Rosemarie. "She's always read books and been so smart."

"I'll build a whole library on the stock market," Jane replied.

But what really turned the trick, and what really made Jane's protests about her brilliance become a whisper, was Eleanor, who joined them about dinner time. Underpaid, still in debt from going to college, Eleanor listened wistfully to the startling news. Sipping her drink, she became wide-eyed as Al assured her she was in the presence of a financial genius. And it was when Eleanor—in the sweetest kind of desperate confidence—asked how to invest $300 she had saved up for summer school that Jane's ambitions suddenly began to take shape.

"I'll help you," Jane told Eleanor in all seriousness and dignity. "I don't yet know how, but I'll find out. You know I will."

Somehow this very need for Jane's prowess made everything official, and a promise beyond one's eager powers to keep may hoist one to undreamed-of powers in trying to keep it.

"I've read somewhere," mused Al, "that brokers call women in the market 'Aunt Jane'. Brother, have you got a head start! You're 'Aunt Jane' from here on."

That did it. From then on it was 'Aunt Jane'. And Jane thrilled to her new moniker the way one thrills to a new status recognized, a new title won.

Yes, what had happened once could happen any number of times. With her sense of urgency coming fast from behind, Jane's fertile mind began compounding figures with the speed of a computer. And while there are nicer ways of saying this, the truth is, she began behaving like an old maid who had just discovered sex.

Some people get that way about the stock market. It invites a new way of thinking, of feeling, and of living—and one wonders how one managed before, without it.

# *TWO*

~~~~~~~~~~~~~~~~~~~~~~~~~~~~~~~~~~~~~~~~~~~~~~~~~~

Since the stock market's hazards are invisible, the beginning investor may pretend they don't exist, and Jane cleared these hazards without so much as pausing for breath. It simply never occurred to her that they had any reason for being there—any more than a cherry in a martini.

Bred and accustomed to looking to men for advice about the higher things, Jane now had only Al and her brother-in-law, who was Rosemarie's banker father in Omaha, and as market advisers, both were as useless as bankers would be expected to be. The brother-in-law took sympathetic note of Jane's situation by also advising a savings account. And Al, hopelessly ambivalent about the market, fought Jane's impulses five days a week and acknowledged her jackpot by encouraging her the other two.

Yet her present mood insulated her from fear. She would have assumed, and could have convinced anyone, that whatever the hazards of the market, they stemmed from ignorance, and ignorance could surely be turned into knowledge. This was partly school teacher talk. But it was conviction, too. Hadn't she seen Horace, who had never played a note or sailed a sea, make himself an authority on the woodwinds and on windjammers? Dear Horace—it seemed so sadly ironic that all this delightful new world had been opened only after his death.

Thanks to her own sorties to the public library, Jane had become expert on the habits of tropical fish and on teen-age psychology—subjects not too unrelated, really, since many fish are predatory and a certain few eat each other alive. Thus both subjects helped her keep on top of the yahoos and junior beatniks who lounged in her substitute classes. But her passion was oriental art, whose delicacy of form and color could move her to tears. And with a few pieces placed here and there, she had lightened and brightened a room full of furniture that had looked grand in the overstuffed thirties. Two exquisite paintings of straight-faced Chinese ancestors hanging over the davenport helped cut *that* monster down to more amenable size, all right. Against the opposite wall a spirited collection of jade horses, cats, and panthers from ancient Persia, China and Egypt took their delicate stance atop an ebony steptable, and *they* reduced the proportions of the other side of the room. Jane and Horace had spent many evenings selecting these authentic replicas from museum catalogs. Thus, beauty served Jane twice—once for balance and once for inspiration.

In other words, there was such a thing as research for a purpose, and Jane's new purpose was not trifling. She was out to catch up with Hetty Green.

Going to the Public Library at Civic Center, she loaded up on books about investing—*How I Made One Million Dollars in the Market in My Spare Time, The Battle for Uncommon Profits,* and *How to be a Sophisticated Investor.* Then, nosing around a newsstand, she spotted a copy of *Barron's National Business and Financial Weekly.* It was both impressive and immediately rewarding, and right away—by airmail—she sent for trial issues of eight advisory services advertised therein. The one she liked best was baited "Three $5 Stocks Poised to Triple." Another that set her mind to spinning was entitled "Two Stocks to Retire On"—although on second thought this ad struck her as loose because it didn't promise *when.*

But Rosemarie thought it looked fine. "You're really going into this, aren't you?" She picked up a two-pound book and flipped the pages. "What do they tell you to do with $25?"

Al and Rosemarie had stopped in to share Playhouse 90 with Jane, and they grabbed every second of the commercials to talk about her future. Since it was a brand new one, it encouraged the exercise of dreams.

"On New Year's days," Al grinned, pulling on his pipe, "you'll have your chauffeur drop off a fifth of champagne for your old pals." A dark, heavy-featured young giant who'd look natural stripped to the waist in a Mediterranean fishing smack, Al was in the mood tonight to feel sweetest benevolence for the marketplace.

Rosemarie speculated, "You'll sit up on Russian Hill in a posh apartment staring at the Golden Gate. You'll lounge around in black velvet pajamas and a diamond choker. Tough." A sudden afterthought and she blurted, "You'll have to get a sterling silver tea service." Her mind flew to her collection of silver services at Gump's. "I'll pick one out for you—one you polished!"

Thumbing through a magazine until he found what he wanted, Al held up an American Express ad for travelers' checks and teased, "Promise you'll never carry more cash than you can afford to lose."

"Promise," Jane crossed her heart. "I'll be like Bob Hope. I'll never carry more than fifty dollars in cash."

Everything could be very gay when Al was not being positively paranoic about Jane's chances. She, of course, loved all the beer-and-pretzel merriment.

Nevertheless, once down to the licklog, Jane was no fool. Her sense of challenge sent little shivers running around the base of her scalp.

"I am," she confessed to Al and Rosemarie, "a babe in the woods. I feel like a Ph. D. candidate about to take his orals."

Being gifted was one thing, but training her gift quite another. She could not really, seriously, put her own and Eleanor's money to soaring without boning up first—and doing whatever else it is one does to get ready for the great battle of financial survival. She had known there was a stock market in about the same way one knows there is an Emperor of Japan and a *Folies Bergères* of Paris. Such legendary institutions hardly clutter up one's daily consciousness.

Her daily consciousness had been formed by a choir-singing mother, a hen-pecked father, and a sedate college major in English. Nothing in all this to help her now. Beyond college, there was her teaching—about as useful to financial know-how as a life lived in a barrel and seen through a bunghole.

As for the influence of Horace—even when he was a boy, his relatives began referring to him as "Poor Horace" and finally, in his adulthood, they consolidated into "Poorhorace." Actually, though, he was a delightfully affectionate, gentle man in an ungentle age—one in ten million—who made the horrendous mistake of assuming it was *what* you knew, not *who,* that was important in getting ahead. The wife he worshipped didn't know any better either.

But lonely women are peculiar—especially, perhaps, lonely women who are the genteel poor. Their sense of adventure dies no sooner than other women's, but merely lies in wait. Inside, they remain spirited and only need something to be spirited about, such as love. In Jane's case, at the moment, nothing beckoned more invitingly than money—which seemed to be the only way to insure her later years against want. Thus, on days free of teaching, which was most of the time, she began to ache for action. Perhaps it was just as well, she decided, that her temporary job at Gump's had ended.

Gazing dreamily out of her front window one noon, she suddenly decided that, at the very least, until she had studied enough to start buying, she ought to see what a brokerage firm looked like. Visiting around would be the laboratory phase of her training, and help give her the feel of things. Seeking the name of a likely firm in the yellow pages of her phone book, she powdered her nose, put on her hat, and was out the door in a flash.

It was a tangy, brilliant day and she walked downhill all the way, humming softly to herself and loving everything in the broad, clean vista before her—especially the beauty of the Bay Bridge and the bevy of Chinese moppets playing hopscotch on a crosswalk. The air had that kind of wine, she thought, that made you feel you were striding downhill whether or not you had a downgrade. Some air has that kind of push.

Reaching Montgomery Street, she fluttered timidly outside the entrance to Sharp and Blarney, which offered the assurance of granite and bronze railings. A little over-awed, she finally opened the massive door a crack. There, through clouds of smoke, she glimpsed a score of silent men standing nailed to the floor, their hats clamped on the back of their heads, their eyes focused in the same direction as if given in to mass hypnosis. Jane was amazed. Where was all that jolly excitement, that stout-hearted reassurance, she had expected? Wasn't any of this *fun?*

Nervously, she entered and the door swung ponderously behind her. Only then, in front of the standees, did she see a circle of chairs containing a small crowd of additional grim and immobile figures, including some well-hatted, middle-aged women. They, too, seemed tense. What was the matter with these investors, Jane asked herself. Were all of them being wiped out? Or hadn't these particular investors studied enough in advance?

Up front, on a circular ramp, three beautiful Chinese girls, dressed in ivory silk pajamas, decoded strange symbols that appeared and reappeared in a frame above their heads. Swiftly, gracefully, they then chalked their translations on a vast circular blackboard. Their smiles reassured Jane.

As she watched them flit about erasing old figures and chalking in the new, Jane fought an impish urge to shout "Bingo!" Yet as she began to absorb the excitement of the people's market, her

Vasiliu

appreciation took on the giddy glaze of Love, believing that each transaction going on before her eyes spun out its own romantic story—of a hope committed, a dream at work, an ambition fired for a loved one. And of a dollar winging its way into the farthest —and the nearest—corner of commerce. Yes, the Chinese girls were taking a barometric reading of people's faith in the future, and like the rope in the Hindu trick, people's profits went up, up, and up.

Finally, exhausted by the steady parading of symbols she did not understand—XYZ, PDQ, and Heaven only knew what else—she smiled at a young man who had softly sidled up to her elbow. Unexpectedly friendly, he introduced himself as Philip Petry, an account executive, and offered her his card, together with a printed announcement of his classes in Learning How to Invest.

"The classes are free," he smiled. "Let me invite you to en- roll, no matter how much experience you've had."

"How wonderful!" she exclaimed, adding hastily, "Oh, yes, I am experienced." She hadn't known such classes eixsted, and the idea was manna from heaven.

With knowledge possessing mountain-moving power, Jane saw in young Mr. Petry about what Queen Isabella must have seen in young Columbus. And if the egg trick young Columbus per- formed demonstrated to Isabella's mind that a continent awaited discovery, Mr. Petry's confident smile made Jane think she could write her own ticket to Paradise. Considering everything he repre- sented, it was all she could do to keep from patting the nice young man on the head. As she finally tore herself away, she sought to identify her unfamiliar emotions. Since they were palpitating with expectancy and hope, she finally decided that what she felt was both a sense of power and adventure—like that of an astronaut trained, helmeted and gazing skyward.

# THREE

~~~~~~~~~~~~~~~~~~~~~~~~~~~~~~~~~~~~~~~~~~~~~~~~~~~

Jane was so keyed up about Mr. Petry's investment course for beginners that she arrived at the lecture room ten minutes before the teacher—with a three-ring notebook and her ballpoint pen backed up with a newly sharpened pencil. Classes were to be held in the Scottish Rites Temple on Van Ness Avenue, and Jane, like a six-year-old on the opening day of school, stood in the foyer until Mr. Petry, swinging his briefcase, walked in hatless with three women following behind him. He and Jane shook hands very formally, and then she and the other ladies, single file, silently followed him into a snug lecture room with large windows. She selected a seat in the center of the front row—her eyes bright with expectancy and her manner as casual as possible under the circumstances.

A customer's man with Sharp and Blarney, Mr. Petry had a cowlick, an Ivy League tie, and the soft, impeccable manners of a mortician. Gravely professional, he laid his dispatch case on a table, rolled a portable blackboard from its corner to the front of the class, checked his chalk and eraser, and then took his seat on a high stool in front of a lectern and gazed in mild wonderment at the middle-aged ladies filing in. Two or three gasped their surprise at seeing each other there, but most were strangers. On the dot at eight o'clock Mr. Petry stood up, cleared his throat, felt the knot of his tie, and waited for complete silence. When the silence reached the breaking point of expectancy, he indulged an engaging smile.

24

"Welcome, fellow investors," he began.

Jane's eyes became damp with appreciation. She loved his getting right down to the spirit of things.

The teacher talked on in a voice surprisingly deep and rich, coming from such a slender chest. And he began, Jane noted, like an oldtime hellfire-and-brimstone minister of the gospel, who put novel ideas of sin into heads that had not contained them before.

"We shall at no time," he emphasized, "mention the word 'speculation' in this class. Nor shall we discuss hot tips, rumors, hearsay. Nor, finally, shall we consider any magic formulas for making money in the stock market. There are none."

All this sounded unnecessarily gloomy, Jane thought. Mr. Petry was not thinking big.

"Instead," he went on, "we shall study a practical system for selecting securities, for making wise decisions, and for protecting our capital with a sound investment program."

With little capital to protect, Jane was feeling a bit left out of things when a woman on the back row snapped her fingers for attention and interrupted Mr. Petry brightly, "Have you heard the difference between 'a speculation' and 'an investment'?"

Mr. Petry, biting obligingly, smiled and said, "No."

"Well," shot back the woman, "An investment is a speculation that didn't pan out."

With a wave of delicious disapproval the class tittered while the teacher frowned. Despite the woman's bad manners, Jane beamed her approval. She found out later that the woman was a psychologist.

Mr. Petry regained control of his class in short order, however, by outlining what he called "an eight-month homework project." And it *was* terrific.

"During the coming eight months," he said, "I would like for each of you to apply the principles you learn here and draw up an imaginary model account. Let us assume that you are investing $25,000." Nobody except Jane seemed to bat an eye at the amount. She wrote it down firmly at the top of a clean page with the caption, "Assumed Capital." Then she retraced her figures several times to build herself up to coping with their size.

Ideally, Mr. Petry opined, the hypothetical list of investments would contain six to eight or even ten common stocks, with one half of their capital invested in "blue chip" securities which, he was careful to point out, were known for their stable quality and their ability to pay dividends through good times and bad.

"Of course," he added, "blue chips are relatively high priced and they offer low yields."

Frowning, Jane wrote in her notebook, "Blue chips over-accepted. Avoid."

"The other half of your hypothetical list," Mr. Petry went on cautiously, "may be in 'growth' securities." While these would entail greater risk, he explained, they also promised greater increase in capital gains—and sometimes," said he, "the gains are sensational."

Seeing Jane brighten and shoot forward in her seat, the teacher paused, measured the gleam in her eyes and soberly warned, "Growth stocks may be loaded with booby traps. Besides, they may pay no dividends at all. But I suppose," he shrugged, "such distribution as I suggest is a good way to learn the hazards." Students could work up any number of lists as they learned more and more and they would be free, of course, to revise from time to time. "But," said Mr. Petry, "I want to see only your final and best list."

Then he archly announced that his own firm of Sharp and Blarney would award a prize to the future investor who achieved the greatest percentage gain by the time the class term ended.

In the buzz of anticipation, the woman on the back row, the psychologist, spoke up with a question that made Jane the teacher squeak with mirth.

"How do you prevent cheating?" she asked. "What's to prevent my consulting old records and just *saying* eight months from now that my best list was also my final one?"

"Well," spluttered Mr. Petry, "the question has never come up . . ."

The psychologist added darkly, "The ego is a powerful instrument. And a prize is at stake."

Nonplussed, the teacher bit his lip and fingered his tie while several class members rumbled against the preposterous idea of cheating and others cautiously weighed the joys of temptation. Finally Mr. Petry asked a helpless question at large. "Any suggestions, any one?"

Having removed temptation from many classrooms, Jane spoke up kindly. "Perhaps we can work in teams of two," she suggested, "with each teammate keeping a record of the other's imaginary transactions."

The teacher shouted his gratitude. "Wonderful! Then each of you can actually work alone, but just—er—benefit by keeping tabs on the other lady's decisions."

So the matter was settled, and before Jane could lean back in her seat the jolly lady to her left plucked at her sleeve and whispered, "Let's you and I be teammates. I'm Mrs. Hope." Mrs. Hope was pink, plump, gay and apparently rich and her very name struck Jane as highly appropriate for anybody heading toward investing. She agreed happily.

Before getting on with his lecture proper, Mr. Petry passed out to his eager pupils the latest editions of monthly stock guides as basic reference material. All of this was so exciting that several ladies squealed out loud. As for Jane, she was beside herself with joy.

Only one thing—a minor thing, after all—was wrong. A snob about good teaching, she felt that Mr. Petry didn't do justice to his wondrous subject matter. He was too matter of fact, too negative. Wondering idly how a magician could ever tire of

magic, she ached to arouse the young man's enthusiasm by re-
counting, ever so casually, what she had just achieved. But, not
wishing her superiority to show so soon, she put off her nagging
urge in favor of observing her classmates.

Of all sizes, shapes and ages, they were about forty in number
and most of them, to Jane's surprise, were middle-aged women
like herself. Word quickly got around the first week, however—
Mr. Petry saw to this—that a few were among San Francisco's
leading business women. In an awed voice, Jane reported to Al
and Rosemarie, "They are women ahead of their time."

There was Miss Gertrude Green, a tall honey-colored corporate
lawyer; Mrs. Helen Spalding, a serious-looking young lovelorn
columnist divorcee; Mrs. Hope, also a divorcee; and a svelte, if
harried, obstetrician whose name Jane didn't catch. Since the
West was three decades behind the East in finding women em-
ployable at all, except as sex objects or symbols, Mr. Petry's class
was truly outstanding.

But the real *crème de la crème* was a Mrs. Henry Hayden-
Critchfield III, a willowy blonde of indeterminate age who was
a onetime dancer, actress and musical comedy soprano. Recently
married to the executive of a wholesale millinery, Mrs. Hayden-
Critchfield now dedicated her talents to displaying her husband's
hats, and her advertising campaign was not what anybody would
call subliminal. Her ravishing headpieces kept the whole class
on edge. In reality, during the first few minutes of each class,
Mr. Petry had a hard go against her competition, particularly since
his star was invariably tardy—and not one to hug the wall and
come in quietly. Mrs. Hayden-Critchfield was "on" all of the
time. She did not merely come in, she made an entrance. In a
wide-brimmed hat she could have served as a beach umbrella.
On her cloche evening all anybody could see of her face was a
widely smiling red mouth. And it was on her cloche evening as
Mrs. Hayden-Critchfield, with throaty apologies, paraded to her
seat with a gliding, ex-chorus girl hitch, that Mr. Petry lost his

class entirely. Standing silent and red-faced, he finally began his lecture over again, from the beginning.

Nevertheless, except for the headpiece entrances and except for the disruptive psychologist, who kept trying to trip the teacher in an error, the girls were ideally orderly pupils. Once settled, they all listened intently, all took verbatim notes in neat notebooks, all nodded gratefully whenever Mr. Petry mildly drove home a point. That is, all except the psychologist, who was too defiant to be taught anything, and Jane, who was too busy being Aunt Jane.

Horace had been fond of saying that Jane was the kind of person she was because she had been born during a sharp, prolonged, dramatic earthquake. A dizzy, black-haired infant loosed upon a world racking in violence would naturally be endowed with a super-ability to take life's curves, he would explain, seriously, exaggerating the earthquake—if not Jane—with gentle humor in his eye. And Horace would have been the first to ask what the stock market could possibly offer that Jane had not already bested by the time she was one hour old. Obviously, the answer is Nothing.

Life's broader practicalities—like knowing when to come in out of the rain—Jane managed with ease and grace; and the smaller, niggling ones she simply looked through, or around, or over. Psychoanalysts call this superior capacity "selective inattention," but then they don't know—as Horace did—that earthquake babies are born with the ability to slough off any complexities. Thus, from the first, Jane was destined to become a sort of editor of life. What she didn't like she was inclined to amend, change, and improve.

Now as a student of the stock market, Jane started right off acting like a fog-cutter romping through the Golden Gate— which means she had the art of making everything happy and promising, with and without Mr. Petry's help.

If Mr. Petry said anything she didn't like, she serenely blotted his pessimism out of her mind as selectively as an editor strikes through a passage. Taking full notes, she thoughtfully amended what he offered and made it her own—often in the form of advice to herself. He warned, "The average doctor can afford to invest more aggressively than the average widow. Therefore his gains will be larger." And Jane, hating the word "widow" and observing the obstetrician's smile, quickly jotted down, "Invest like a doctor." When Mr. Petry said ever so tentatively, "We may be on the verge of a second Industrial Revolution," Jane wrote, "Buy for revolution." When he said, "During our history, the market has gone up more often than down," she wrote "America *is* a bull market." When he advised, "Only the foolhardy try to outguess the market," she wrote, "What's so sacred about the market? Starting with the weatherman and the doctor, everybody guesses at everything everyday."

Of Mrs. Lucrezia Hope, her teammate, Jane did not altogether approve—particularly when the divorcee embarrassed Mr. Petry by bringing him flowers from her garden and hanging upon his every word with teen-age fascination. Still, Jane could not resist her high spirits. Whenever Mrs. Hope felt compelled to make a note, she whispered a jolly "Cripes!" sounding so emotional Jane reserved her estimate of her teammate's value as a stock market technician.

Since Mrs. Hope called Dallas home, practically daily, Jane was some time in learning her friend had left Dallas twenty years before to marry a Californian. But Jane was no time at all in learning that her new friend considered California as great a mess as her marriage—maintaining that the only nice thing about San Francisco was the ladies' room at I. Magnin's. Said Mrs. Hope, "Reminds me of Buckingham Palace." Jane didn't quite dare ask exactly how well Mrs. Hope *knew* Buckingham Palace.

To Jane's right sat the only man in the class, and he introduced himself as Wally Googins. "Call me Wally," he invited right away, and Jane was impressed with his friendliness. He also aroused her curiosity; for oddly enough, he seemed bored in class, and spent far more time looking over the students than listening to anything the teacher said.

Wally himself cleared up this little mystery at the end of the first class hour, when he walked a few blocks down Van Ness with Jane. Calling himself "an investment man," he grinned broadly, "Better not tell Professor Petry, but I enroll in investment classes now and then to get to know people and build up my clientele. The professor might not like this idea. He wants everybody himself."

Jane supposed Wally's idea was very shrewd. After all, business is business, and the young man was at least ambitious.

Wally was a tall young man of twenty-eight or so, with dark eyes, a vibrant voice, a brilliant smile like Cary Grant's, and a lightweight touch with heavy drama. As he and Jane walked along the brilliantly lighted street, he described his own firm, Van Dyke and Buchanan, explaining conspiratorially, "We deal only in special situations." Pausing for effect, he went on in a low voice, "Of course we seek out special situations *very* carefully."

Jane let out a cry of sheer delight.

Wally added confidentially, "They're hard to find. Sometimes we spend months studying—studying and waiting for them to mature just right for the picking." He snapped his fingers to indicate the proper degree of doneness.

When she and Wally separated at a street corner to go their separate ways, she kept right on adoring the sound of "special situations." They must be imaginative. She also liked Wally. He had an impudent charm, there was no doubt of it. The evening Mrs. Hayden-Critchfield III came "on" in a flowered hat, Wally said aloud, "My God, she'll have every bee on the West Coast following 'er." The actress-dancer-soprano smiled broadly and bowed in Wally's direction.

Wally's eye for dress extended, good naturedly, to his own

effects, which were sometimes startling. Partial to bow ties, he used them either to dress up or dress down his sporty vests, which took some doing. By the end of his first two weeks in class, Jane observed with a growing sense of awe that he had worn a different vest almost every session. One that took her eye was a tattersall black and red check on a white background, in fine corduroy—balanced smartly by a severe black tie.

"Sharp, uh?" Wally inquired. "I've got to do as well as our chorus girl."

"You look," Jane replied, proud of keeping up, "very cool."

Wally added seriously, "I wear them to express the optimism, the verve, of my firm. At Van Dyke and Buchanan, we don't go around looking like undertakers." Wally loved to hoot at Mr. Petry's somber dress.

As the weeks went by, Wally made a chivalrous point of escorting one pupil after another to her home—that is, whenever he came to class, for he played hookey now and then. During the class break, however, when everybody ran out for a cigarette or a breath of fresh air, Wally occasionally escorted Jane across the street to Otto's for a quick cup of coffee. Otto's was a snack bar so small it boasted only counter space, and Jane loved climbing onto a high bar stool, hooking her heels into the footring, and chatting with Wally, even hurriedly. He had unexpected talents.

One evening, learning that she taught English, Wally confessed he was given to reading poetry aloud, and during class break that night he insisted that they rush to Otto's. There he showed off by reciting from Edwin Markham's *Lincoln, the Man of the People*.

"'Here,'" Wally dramatically declaimed, setting his cup down hard, "'Here was a man to hold against the world, A man to match the mountains and the sea.'"

"How perfectly beautiful," sighed Jane.

"Ah," Wally shook his head solemnly, "America needs such heroes today."

A lump came to Jane's throat as Wally, carried away, mixed in a little Vachel-Lindsay *Lincoln:* " 'Yes, when the sick world cries, how can he sleep?' " Giving in to his despondent question, Wally sat with his head propped in his hands. They were ten minutes late getting back to class that evening, which made Mr. Petry frown. With some testiness he pointed out that class break was normally ten to twelve minutes. Did the class wish to expand it to twenty? Jane blushed, but Wally said, "Our apologies, Professor."

After this petty crime shared, this burst of camaraderie, the two took to writing notes to each other in class, when Mr. Petry wasn't looking. This struck Jane as friendly and fun, and made her feel young again—especially when Mrs. Hope would reach over, intercept the note and add her bit. Wally was a terrible speller, true, but so were most young people these days. Frowning upon today's flash card methods of teaching the 3 R's, Jane had long considered her own generation the last to lay claim to literacy. Still, she reminded herself fairly, George Washington was reputed to be a bit irregular with his letters.

\* \* \* \* \*

One night after Jane reached home, she knocked on Eleanor's door to catch up on her news.

Down on the floor in her pajamas, trying to figure out a game to give her kindergartners, Eleanor's fresh and innocent face looked so alive with animation that an idea popped into Jane's head from nowhere. Why hadn't she thought of this before, she wondered. After all, Eleanor was a newcomer to San Francisco, with little chance to get acquainted. Thus Jane heard herself saying aloud, "I've met a nice young man I think you would like, dear, and I'm going to arrange for you to meet!" With a burst of anticipation she added, "You would take to him, I know!"

Resisting an impulse—perhaps because a tiny voice within

her noted that the less an avowed matchmaker says about prospects, the better—this is all Jane said about Wally. Being casual is the thing, and keeping the focus broad. "You should know more young men," she said.

Eleanor acknowledged her handicap with a shrug. "Kindergarten teachers don't meet any men over five!" she said philosophically.

Jane went home that night fired with enthusiasm. And the image in her mind before she gave herself to sleep was of Eleanor's expressive little face—and of Wally's latest vest. Tonight, sporting an outlandish green and orange paisley in Viyella, he had written to Jane, "Dig this vest. Now can I compete with our musical comedy star?" And she had replied, "Not until you can match it with a beret."

Yes, Eleanor needed more lightheartedness. There were things in life—yes, a lot of things—as important as spelling.

As Jane lay in bed, her light out, and Kim curled at her feet, she permitted herself to miss Horace poignantly—his thoughtfulness, his wry humor. Then, resolutely, telling herself one must keep on going forward, she turned her thoughts to her new friends, her new hopes.

Down the hall, at that very same moment, Eleanor was lying in bed thinking to herself, " '*Mister*' Petry. That's all I've ever heard. I wonder what his first name is."

# *FOUR*

~~~~~~~~~~~~~~~~~~~~~~~~~~~~~~~~~~~~~~~~~~~~~~~~~~~~~~

The next evening, without a class to go to, Jane became lonely and restive and decided to drop in on Al and Rosemarie. Finding them at the kitchen table pasting their Green stamps from their supermarket, she reached for a booklet and sponge and began giving them a hand.

"We're thinking of turning them in for a house and lot," said Rosemarie gaily.

"Yeah," Al grunted. "A pad over Belvedere way. That'll be about the time I'm made president of the Bank of America."

While Jane brought them up to date on her progress as a student of the market, Al put on the teakettle to make instant coffee. At the mention of Wally and his divine special situations, however, Al looked up sharply.

"Aunt Jane, you keep an eye on that lad," he warned. "He looked like a slicker to me."

Jane laughed. "You have hardly seen Wally. He's a perfect dear." Actually, Al had met Wally one night in a downpour. Al had come for Jane in his car and had given Wally a lift too, and Jane wouldn't forget it soon, if only because Wally had laughed at Al's calling her "Aunt Jane." The next class hour Wally had promptly told Mrs. Hope of the nickname—and Mrs. Hope had told all the others, who then adopted it.

Recalling the results to Al and Rosemarie, Jane smiled. "I'd never expected to be an aunt to a Texan or an investment man! But there you are."

They could tell she was pleased. The moniker seemed to give her market ambitions a certain validity.

Pretty soon Eleanor came in and sat down to help. "This is like my kindergarten," she said, but the sigh that followed seemed to surprise even herself.

"You ought to be out having fun instead of pasting stamps, a child as pretty as you." Jane's idea about introducing Wally had emboldened her to speak up, get Eleanor in psychological trim, as it were.

Unaware of Jane's new ambition, Al looked at Eleanor as if seeing her for the first time. Alongside his tall, slender Rose-marie, Eleanor was little, all right, as well as cute—with freckles trotting across the bridge of her nose and her blond hair clasped in a pony tail. And because this was her first year of teaching, her three friends were always hovering to help out with her problems, which weighed heavily.

Now Eleanor stopped pasting and gave them all a supplicating look. "Thus far," she began, trying a smile, "a kindergarten teacher seems to have two kinds of days—dry days and wet days—like today. We had a little accident. Little Patty Jergens does get so excited when we march to music."

Al hollered with laughter, but Jane shushed him.

"That could be a sign of talent," she said wryly, and quoted a noted authority.

By midnight, with everybody still madly pasting stamps, Al summed up with satisfaction, "Hottest assembly line in San Francisco." They had stacked up ten full books, and their achievement gave Jane such a good feeling that she went home full of plans and purpose. She had listened to enough of Mr. Petry's principles in class; she was bursting to get to her home-work—her hypothetical portfolio.

She set up a card table by the windows overlooking the street and spread out the three notable books on investing, together with a flock of advisory services. She and Mrs. Hope were swapping their varied market letters, which would help her create her list for Mr. Petry. Stealing a look at their promising headlines, she went to bed and smiled in her sleep.

Early the next morning Eleanor rapped on the door and came in to show off her frivolous new white gloves adorned with pleated ruffles.

"Under your influence I've gone out and bought something I can't afford!" she exclaimed. "You see," she smiled, "I do have faith."

Jane was astonished to realize how disturbed she was by Eleanor's faith. "I wouldn't care so much for myself," she admitted softly. "But I couldn't bear not to make a lot of money for you." Her lips trembled. Brave little Eleanor, still head over heels in debt.

Eleanor laughed. "But you forget what a born shopper you are. You've taught me the best time to buy everything. Sheets at January White sales, turkeys in September. What's so different about stocks?"

Jane hadn't quite thought of this angle, but she remembered the time—it was in April—when the two had gone marketing together and she had spotted artichokes in Eleanor's grocery cart.

"Fall, late fall," she had protested, "is the time to buy artichokes." Eleanor had promptly put them back and substituted squash.

Now brightening, Jane played variations on Eleanor's theme as if it had been her idea all along. "September's best food buys," she affirmed, "are turkeys, grapes and pears. January's are eggs, apples, sweet potatoes." The idea was so good it brought color rushing to her cheeks.

"The only trick," said Eleanor, "is to find September's turkeys on the stock market!" Looking hastily at her watch, she blew Jane a kiss and dashed out the door.

Hurrying through breakfast and adding the financial pages of the day's *San Francisco Chronicle* to her work table, Jane opened her notebook to record the wisdom of the Wall Street pundits. The morning was sunny, her day was free of engagements, and she sparked to her workout like a child to a merry-go-round.

Now most scholars of the market, when all keyed up to select their stocks, study prospects on the basis of their earnings record, their dividends, the ratio of their price to their earnings, and their outlook. But Jane McPhipps shrugged off the usual rules as mere guidelines for the less talented. Besides, she wanted to be more than just acquisitive. She also wanted to be expressive, creative.

Telling herself there is a proper key to fit any puzzle, she wanted *her* solutions to soar above and beyond all the tiresome things Mr. Petry kept talking about, such as birth rate and freight car loadings. But, before settling on her own ideas, she admitted, reluctantly, she would first have to study others. And so, burying herself in the books—which were riddled by charts—she bravely sallied into unknown waters.

They all but sank her bodily. All she had wanted to do was to sift out a few consistent guides to intelligent investing. These she would embroider upon, in expressing her own personal credo. But at the end of three books that took her three days to digest, here are the main rules the various investment authorities advised their readers to observe:

> Investing is an art.
>
> Investing is a science.
>
> Speculation is a healthy thing. After all, Henry Ford speculated with his Tin Lizzie.
>
> If you speculate, you will invariably lose your money.

Don't follow the crowd. The crowd is always wrong.

Don't buy a stock that isn't popular, and don't *you* be the one to try making it popular. Let the crowd act first. Then buy when it's attracting most attention.

Diversification of investments is a necessary safeguard.

Diversification is nonsense. It is both a thin protection against poor knowledge and a prime diluter of profits.

Invest only in established blue chips.

Stay away from blue chips; they may be tired and they very likely come too dear. Buy a blue chip before it becomes one.

Don't buy after a stock split is common knowledge.

It's a good idea to buy into an announced split. You can count on a quick rise.

If you don't know what else to do with a stock, sell it. Be a trader. There are always better buys.

The best time to sell a good stock is never. Nobody ever made profits by trading.

Dollar averaging is the most sophisticated approach to higher profits.

Dollar averaging is throwing good
money after bad.

Be sure to buy stocks that are popular with investment trusts. Then
you can be sure of their quality.

The fact that investment trusts hold
certain stocks means they cost too
much to buy. Rather, buy an un-
popular stock whose price is still
low.

Avoid stop-loss orders. They're a
nasty trap on the downside.

Insure your profits with stop-loss orders, the way the professionals do.

Not even an editor with Jane's experience could do anything
about such a blizzard of contradictions.

Even more wildly confusing were most of the bird-dogging
weekly advisory letters, which made investors think they had
only seven days to act. Jane spent a couple of days comparing
the prolific *littérateurs* of Wall Street's special advisory mail
services and, to be sure of a wide sampling, she went out and
poked around in the research library of Sharp and Blarney. For
all the good it did her, Mr. Petry beamed and told her he was
gratified to see such scholarly effort.

Some weekly letters were folksy and altruistic, and bent on
helping a neighbor parlay his nest egg of $200 into a cozy $2000.
Others were as impersonal as so many blank checks. And while
a few were immodestly know-it-all, most were maddeningly in-

decisive. One particularly useless letter haughtily quoted classical Greek, touched upon Zen-Buddhism, cited sample portfolis of $100,000, and for its recommendations of purchases sought refuge in the subjunctive mood. "Oil shares," it pussyfooted, "may offer a tempting shelter." *Who* under the sun, Jane asked herself, wants a *shelter?*

Since none of the experts could really agree on what was *going* to happen, Jane undertook an unusual experiment. One night, laying a whole batch of advisory letters side by side, she began to compare their comments on what had *already* happened for the financial world to see and measure. But her attempt to learn what she assumed was empirical knowledge merely exploded on its launching pad.

From her first three authorities (and she saw little point in going any further) she gleaned these conclusions on the past week's market activities:

The first said: "It was a week of considerable nervousness—and clearly a round for the bears."

The second offered, "The week's bullish upthrust into new high ground did much to overwhelm the bears."

The third and calmest source noted, "Stocks merely churned last week."

More ignorant and more dashed than ever, her eyes smarting from her days of effort, Jane found herself seized by a peculiar sensation. She seemed to be standing in the dark at the top of the stairs—and the stairs were covered with roller skates.

She ached to do something violent. Then she began missing Horace again—who would have told her, gently, to take it easy. Finally, shrugging, she carefully winnowed two temperate, scholarly letters from the score or more in front of her and threw the remainder onto the floor for Kim to play with. With his back arched and his tail high in the air, Kim pounced. He loved to shred paper.

But Jane did hang on to the two. Both of them flattered the

investor by assuming he wanted detailed knowledge, not sooth-saying; and both avoided a too literal faith in Dow's orthodoxy. But what appealed most to their critical reader—neither letter writer seemed compelled to make a recommendation just because a weekly issue was due. Indeed one came out flat-footed and said, Stay liquid until such time as we *can* recommend; and the other used a few more words to say the same thing. Neither was a man to be pushed around in the market by a journalistic dead-line, and Jane heartily approved their spirit.

Even so, these two radicals were not enough to keep her from reaching for her notebook, and she bore down so hard she broke the new point on her pencil. "Frightening lack of togetherness in expert opinion," she wrote. "Better to trust self."

# *FIVE*

~~~~~~~~~~~~~~~~~~~~~~~~~~~~~~~~~~~~~~~~~~~~~~~~~~

Eleanor brought in salad and popovers to go with Jane's fresh tuna, and the two had early supper while blessing Brawny Tony, a commercial fisherman, another former pupil of Jane's. He had never understood Edgar Allen Poe or even those few early American writers who used more reasonable vocabularies; naturally, when Jane forgot to flunk him and let him honorably graduate, he became her slave for life. Even today, years later, Tony took pleasure in calling her every six months or so from Fisherman's Wharf, where he docked his 54-foot *Isabella*. "This your bad boy!" he always bellowed. Jane, wincing, had to hold the receiver away from her ear. "You gotta plenty tuna an' salmon?"

Tony also gave her a list of fisherman friends who would sell her salmon right off their boats, when he wasn't around. "This 'a illegal," he assured her cheerfully, "But so my diplome." Neatly editing out the illegal part, Jane made an occasional run to Fisherman's Wharf, bought for next to nothing, and always came home in high spirits to share her prize with her neighbors. Eleanor would whip potatoes, Rosemarie toss the salad, Al man the beer, and Jane poach the salmon. These were always gay evenings, even though, as Eleanor said, there was no point in listening to Jane and Al on the same subject. They just canceled each other out.

"Fisherman's Wharf has the loveliest, most bracing smells in the world," Jane would declaim, with more poetry than truth.

44

"They come from the Seven Seas." And Al would protest, "It stinks like hell."

But this was a Thursday night, the stores were open, Rosemarie and Al had to work, Jane had to leave shortly for class, and despite Tony's gift, she felt sad and boxed in. "The more I read," she confessed to Eleanor, "the less I know. I have studied again all day, and all I have learned is some gobbledygook." She got up to clear the table.

Eleanor, looking pert in leotards and, after a wonderful meal, quite philosophical, merely opined, "Couldn't be any sillier than the educators'."

With mock gravity, Jane asked, "Do you or don't you teach 'the whole child'?"

"No! I teach 'im in parts. An elbow, a heel, a tummy."

"Well, you've heard nothing yet." Jane raised her voice and pounded out the rhythm of the words on the table. "Wait until you've heard *rally, boom, bust, topping out, breakthrough point.* Wall Street lingo is as noisy as little boys in a vacant lot." She added, "There's a menagerie too. Dogs, cats, bulls and bears."

"Maybe," Eleanor ventured, "the market needs a few more women like you, Aunt Jane. You could help tone things down a bit."

Jane agreed that this was a possibility, but her heart wasn't in it. Deep inside, she knew, she was cross with her tutors, the experts. It did seem to her that their fiscal contrariness was more than a dedicated pupil should be asked to bear. Maybe she'd never get anywhere. But this thought was too dismal to tolerate, and she tried to bury it.

Eleanor suddenly broke into the gloom with a question. It was casual enough. "Who," she asked, "is Wally?"

Guiltily, realizing she had done nothing about introducing Eleanor and Wally, Jane replied, forcing the casualness, "Oh, he's just a nice classmate. Lots of fun."

How could a matchmaker manage with any finesse, she wondered, and without frightening one's prospects half to death? Since Wally seemed so systematically busy about escorting all the other ladies home, she could think of no good reason for inviting him to her apartment. He hadn't bothered to bring *her* home, she assumed, because they visited together during class.

"He's working so hard," said Jane admiringly, "to build his clientele as a broker."

"I wish you weren't going to school tonight!" Eleanor said plaintively. "I do hate Thursday nights. Everybody's busy but me."

"Come go to class with me!" Jane was ecstatic. Why hadn't this idea occurred to her before? "Visitors are welcome. Mr. Petry greets them all as future students, future commissions." Jane clinched her point. "After all, it's your money too."

"What," asked Eleanor, her eyes sparkling, "is Mr. Petry's first name?"

"Philip. It's Philip O. Petry."

"Oh," giggled Eleanor, "his initials spell 'POP'."

At Jane's urging, she rushed to change to her soft pink and grey polka dot with a winged pink bow at her throat. One look at her when she reappeared and Jane wanted to jump for joy.

"You look," she said, "like an angel poised for flight. I just hope you take to him."

It was a brilliant evening with low stars, and the two walked up the long hill to Van Ness Avenue and finally entered the building just behind Mr. Petry. Gloating like a mother hen with a chick in tow, Jane introduced her guest to the teacher and left the two together while she ran ahead to look for Wally. She had never mentioned Eleanor to Wally; she was awaiting the right moment. Well, this was it, willy-nilly. The class was all assembled and expectant, all but Wally. He was nowhere in sight.

With sinking heart, Jane tried to shy away from Mrs. Hope, who rushed up to show her latest transaction. An undaunted believer in learning by doing, Mrs. Hope gaily confessed, "My lists aren't make believe, Aunt Jane. I'm *really* buying and selling —and having a whee of a time!"

Noting a loss of $553, Jane remonstrated, "But buying a stock is the *last* thing you do! First, you learn!" She knew Mrs. Hope couldn't possibly understand why she hadn't yet shown her a list of any kind. After all, Mr. Petry expected the teammates to keep in close touch.

Ducking away from her impetuous partner, Jane turned to look for Wally, and at that moment Eleanor and Mr. Petry walked in. As Jane saw him smile at Eleanor she also heard him say, "We have a lot in common! We both teach the ABC's!" Whatever else he said was too low for her to catch above Mrs. Hope's burbling about her new hair tint, which was a Maxfield Parrish pink, but she did hear Eleanor say, "Oh, thank you," and saw her smile dazzlingly.

Bounding toward Jane, Eleanor squeezed her hand and whispered, "You are so right, Aunt Jane. He's wonderful!"

Stunned into silence, Jane finally managed a crooked smile. It was also a deflated one, but she let things go at that. Anyway, Philip Petry was a nice, if colorless, boy, utterly lacking in Wally's fire and imagination. Wally would go much farther in life. Bracing her shoulders against her seat, Jane muttered a muted, refined "Damn," and resolved to go right ahead with her original idea.

During the next two hours of class her resolution wavered, but not too much, in the course of Mr. Petry's surprise lecture. Exposing a wholly new self, Philip O. Petry began to be casual, urbane, even light in his touch. As if explaining the subject of investments solely to Eleanor, he smiled at her and remarked in a droll voice, "In this business, anybody who is one hundred per cent right thirty per cent of the time is a whiz kid, and rates alongside J. P. Morgan." Still on the negative side, Jane observed, but suddenly ingratiatingly human about it. Once he said, "Sometimes when people start thinking about method, they get all loused up."

Mrs. Hope, alert to his shining new appeal, whispered to Jane, "*Sacré Bleu!* What's happened to my boy? He's acting human as a Texan!" Jane whispered back, "He's always better when Wally isn't here." And this was true. The two young men did not cotton to one another. Mischievous as Wally was, he loved to throw curved questions at the teacher. "I don't think that's it at all," said Mrs. Hope, with a wink. "That explanation doesn't satisfy me!"

Neither, really, was Jane satisfied. She knew only too well what was happening. As a teacher she had seen the attention of a new girl in class make the dullest bumpkin come to life; and a new boy put color in the cheeks of the drabbest little sparrow. And she considered it definitely established that a direct connection existed between the confident, even strutting Mr. Petry and Eleanor, who now sat in Wally's seat beside her drinking in every word.

Even so, she disapproved of Mr. Petry's lecture that evening. His subject, "Buying for Income," dealt with the stable dividend blue chips, which he called "the widow's blessing," and *that* word set Jane's pencil to impertinent doodling. Having heard all this before, anyway, from most of the experts, she deliberately let her mind wander to the two heretics who had delighted her soul by demonstrating how higher-yielding companies concentrating on growth had consistently made more money for their stockholders than the stable high-yield securities. What would Philip O. Petry say to that? Whatever he would say, this marked a milestone in Jane's research. With her pencil she had calculated how an investment in 100 shares of New Frontier Rocket Riders, purchased at $15 a share in 1954, had now grown to 350 shares worth $18,000—and well, that was the kind of thing that kept Jane at her books.

Why didn't the teacher even mention such goodies? The

question perplexed Jane until she thought of her own field of education. There she had heard an impatient professor demonstrate that a bright idea conceived at educational headquarters usually took half-a-century before it became respectable enough to trust in the average classroom. All of which showed the power of entrenched interests, the guardians of inertia, who were eternally frightened by new ideas. Was there, perhaps, a parallel? Jane smiled to herself.

Securities paying the highest dividends were not her cup of tea. Permitting her attention to return to Mr. Petry, she finally dispatched the whole idea with a cheery entry in her notebook. "Brokers full of dogma. Income stocks are for the birds. Buy something with giddyap." She didn't think the moment exactly favorable for showing her conclusions to Eleanor.

After class Mr. Petry sought out Eleanor "to finish our chat about teaching." And while the two said goodbye and walked off in one direction, Jane walked in another. Mr. Petry had offered to drive her home, but Jane said she needed exercise.

She also needed to think. She could just see Al's and Rosemarie's faces when she told them how frustrated and vexed she was.

By the time she had reached her friends' door, however, she had undergone a change of heart, for now she could see the miscarriage of her plan as teeming with promise for the future, to say the least, when she would succeed in introducing Wally. So, swearing Al and Rosemarie to secrecy, she wound up telling them everything. Rosemarie, in blue pajamas, pursed her pink lips in thoughtfulness, but Al threw back his head and roared.

"You are a no-good busybody!" he said.

Rosemarie started choosing up sides. "I'm for Wally," she announced flatly, having met neither young man. "I want it to be Wally."

Al snorted. "You women! My God, they haven't even laid eyes on each other, and you're tuning up for the wedding!"

Jane admitted, "We've seen far too much television."

His point won, Al could go on, and he began plumping for Phil Petry. "He's at least a straight shooter. I don't like the smell of Wally's 'special situation'. I just hope he doesn't throw you a lure."

"Tell you what," proposed Rosemarie, ignoring Al. "Eleanor can have first one to dinner, then the other. And we can all help pass on 'em."

"Eleanor does, you know, have quite a little head of her own," Al put in sourly. Then he brightened, "Still it would be a chance for a hell of a good party." Al loved any excuse for a party.

"Now don't," begged Jane, "do anything to prejudice the child against Wally."

Once home, Jane decided to wait up for Eleanor and finally, at one o'clock, Eleanor knocked softly at her door. Standing in the half-light of the doorway, her face flushed with excitement, she looked like a soft pink glow of dreams that did not necessarily promise to advance the cause of teaching.

"We went dancing at the Palace Corner!" she exclaimed. "It was divine." Even her voice was dreamy.

"Saturday night," she went on, making no effort to sound casual, "Phil wants to take me to North Beach to see all the Beatniks."

Jane couldn't resist smiling, "All this sounds like two young teachers doing lively professional research."

Eleanor laughed and shyly kissed her good night. "You are so wonderful to do this for me."

That night Jane lay awake in a speculative mood. Was it possible, she wondered, that young Philip Petry was less negative than she had believed?

# *SIX*

~~~~~~~~~~~~~~~~~~~~~~~~~~~~~~~~~~~~~~~~~~~~~~~~~~~~~~~~~~~~~~~

Frustrated in her struggle to make sense out of the experts, thwarted by foul luck in her attempts at matchmaking, Jane welcomed an early morning phone call from the principal of the Golden Gate High School, asking her to fill in for a case of appendicitis for a couple of weeks. Here was something she could do.

She showered and dressed, ate a quick breakfast, rode a bus for thirty minutes, and finally confronted her first class, the first of five groups of teen-agers committed by the laws of California to the study of American Literature. She smiled, told them her name, took the roll, and got briskly down to business.

Utterly possessed by struggling against the rougher realities of life, she didn't feel like putting up with overyoung students hell-bent on trying out a substitute teacher. ("Testing their new environment," the supervisors always called it.) Especially when a six-footer volunteered in a croaking voice, as the class tittered, "Ma'am, Miss Catton never give us homework or themes to write."

This was all it took to trigger Jane's luxurious impulse to begin teaching as forthrightly as she always hankered to. Believing that teen-agers in a literature course ought at least to be able to *read*, and finding that most of them couldn't, she flabbergasted them by putting them to exercises in remedial reading. At first this seared their souls. But in three days, by showing firm purpose, a ready smile, patience where needed, and relentless vigilance, she won over the bright students, encouraged the average, and injured the dull ones not a bit.

Jane had once been criticized by a snooping supervisor for wading into first things first, and had it not been for a militant spirit on the School Board, she might have been in trouble. A Mrs. August Ernst, now deceased, had been mad enough to say in print—just about that time—that the schools' amiable ineffectuality ought to be investigated. Mrs. Ernst had come out foursquare against drum majorettes, boys who made fudge instead of studying physics, and liberty that had turned into license. Jane had often wished she had written a thank-you note to Mrs. Ernst, who had died shortly afterward from high blood pressure.

But now, as an offset to her struggles with the adolescent age, she turned her attention in her spare time of evenings to a question that had nagged her ever since she had taken up her study of the market. Specifically, she wanted to learn what Mr. Charles Dow had in mind when he invented his mysterious theory. Dow was to the market as Einstein was to physics—and hadn't Einstein unlocked forces of unimaginable power? Maybe an understanding of the Dow Theory was all that was holding her back.

At her card table in the evenings, resisting the blandishments of her neighbors, Jane began another siege of study—this time for Al too. He had amazed her by saying he wanted to know all about Dow.

At first Jane considered it a corking idea that Mr. Dow, even as long ago as 1897, had tied the kite of the rail stocks to the price averages of certain industrial stocks. Nodding her approval, she thought this showed remarkable insight. After all, if the economy is to prosper, goods have to be shipped. That was the first thing.

But it was the *next* thing that captivated her, hook, line and sinker. Now *this* was genius: it was the way these two averages sang *together* that gave the Dow theorists their clarion cue to the market's immediate future. Singly, neither one meant anything; but together they outdid Nostradamus in their power to foretell. There was no doubt about it. The Dow theorists said so.

Jane was so set up about all this that she should have let well enough alone and never opened her second book. For therein, crass as you please, some bumptious authority showed that the only trouble with the Dow Theory was that practically none of its followers agreed with one another on what the averages were saying. One authority would call a certain cue a sure signal for a bear market, but another would see the same cue a rallying call for the bulls. Apparently, Jane reflected, you could get any answer you wanted if only you sought the right oracle. In short, she gathered that Dow men could never really tell whether the market was heading up or heading down—a point of difference that struck her as pretty pertinent. And as she calculated, any investor hapless enough to have heeded the theory's classical buy and sell signals since the Black October of 1929 would have been wrong 15 times out of 24.

It was enough to give rise to cruelest disillusionment, and for the first time Jane seriously questioned the power of knowledge over the market place. Even so, she couldn't help viewing Dow's followers with kindly pity. Dow wasn't the only Great Man to leave a scholarly hassle behind him. Look at the mess Freud left behind. Or John Dewey. Or, for that matter, Christ.

Her own conclusion about the Dow theory she thought worth proposing as a graduate dissertation to the Harvard School of Business, for what was wrong became perfectly clear to her. All it needed was modernizing. The great man had thought his deep thoughts in an era of gaslight, slow freight and long before the days of piggyback—not to mention swift technological change. What somebody ought to do, she thought, was to get the whole up-to-date story on the way goods are shipped today. Everybody knew the trucking industry was wrecking the rails. Why shouldn't trucking figure in? Charmed with her contribution, Jane's mind raced to include air freight and river barges, which the Dow theorists also too often ignored. Then for good measure she tossed in her imaginings about the magic of technology—which made dry clouds rain, salt water fresh, and night turn into day. And she idly guessed that such phenomena, in the marketplace, were not likely to be confined by anybody's theory.

For several days Jane couldn't bring herself to say anything to Al about the Dow Theory, if only because he had always thought she was teacher enough to explain almost anything with intelligence. But one evening while she was puttering around and feeding Kim, Al banged on the kitchen wall, and she imagined the time had come.

Going next door to the Bonelli's, she found Rosemarie doing her nails and Al gathering up office work he had been doing on the kitchen table—and, standing above him, Jane noticed for the first time that Al was balding. Since Horace had always said Al was the age of the son they might have had, she felt unexpectedly emotional about this, but said nothing.

He got up and poured her a glass of wine, which she accepted gratefully. Then he said, "All right, all right, Aunt Jane. What's with Dow? Give."

"Oh, I've heard of Dow!" Rosemarie volunteered brightly. "Mr. Figbee, our floorwalker, watches something he calls 'Dow' all the time. You kind of keep score with it, or something. Don't you?"

Jane replied thoughtfully. "'Keeping score' is close enough, really. Only it doesn't tell you what's going to happen until *after* it's happened. And then nobody agrees on what actually did happen." To her own amazement, she realized she was not exaggerating.

Rosemarie looked puzzled and Al looked disappointed. Finally he asked, "No good to you?"

"No good," said Jane. She took a sip of wine. "But I must say," she added cheerfully, "that the Dow is a marvelous example of the lengths grown men will go to keep themselves occupied. I daresay there's an unbelievable number who'd perish if they didn't have their Dow averages to watch."

Finally, back home, Jane took her sharpest pencil and wrote a reminder in her notebook for a less busy day, "Update Dow."

# *SEVEN*

~~~~~~~~~~~~~~~~~~~~~~~~~~~~~~~~~~~~~~~~~~

Wally and Jane fell into the habit of dropping into Otto's after class for a leisurely cup of coffee—that is, when Wally was not taking some of the other ladies home—and lately Wally frequently dragged her along to a nearby showroom that displayed sporty little British automobiles. Thus one night in class Jane wasn't a bit surprised when he wrote, "Want to ride home tonight in my new Triumph?" Her spirits leapt. She endorsed the note, "Love to," and handed it back.

During class break she hurried to a telephone booth in the lobby to call Eleanor. Eleanor would be at home that night; after all, Mr. Petry was teaching. For two weeks now, ever since Eleanor had visited class, she and Phil Petry had been together every evening except class night.

Whispering mysteriously over the telephone, Jane gave Eleanor intense and precise instructions. "Be at my place when I get home. Do have on those toreador pants I disapprove of. And do have fresh coffee made." Returning to her seat by Wally, she sat through the remainder of the lecture in a state of rapt titillation.

From the beginning of this evening, Mr. Petry had been profoundly moved by his sense of mission, and not even Mrs. Hayden-Critchfield's plumed beret had made a dent against it. Impressed by his earnestness, Mrs. Hope whispered to Jane, "*Merde!* Isn't he cute? And look at his new Countess Mara tie!"

Mrs. Hope had x-ray eyes for everything about Mr. Petry. All Jane could make out about his tie was a mauve field with white scriggles on it. When she observed that they looked like staphylococci, Mrs. Hope giggled out loud.

Mr. Petry's theme was the over-the-counter market of securities —stocks that are not listed on any exchange, and the girls braced themselves to grasp the ins-and-outs of their marketability. With her mind elsewhere, Jane did not pay much attention until she heard him say, "You need not avoid a stock just *because* it trades 'over-the-counter'. It *may* be a stable income payer." Taking Mr. Petry's pessimism as a splendid signal, she jotted down, "Look into over-the-counter stocks. They must have giddyap."

After class she and Wally left hurriedly, Wally's hand tugging at her elbow, and raced two blocks up Sutter Street where the car was parked. Bowing low, Wally opened the door of a fire-engine red, black-topped Triumph convertible, and joyously, she fitted herself into the little bucket seat beside him. Gunning the car up the hill, Wally pushed a button, put the top down, and went roaring up to Twin Peaks to show her the city below.

In the ivory blue of the moonlight, the city's lights shone like diamonds, and as impatient as Jane was to get Wally home to Eleanor, she surrendered herself to a blissful mood of serenity. It was good to relax, forget it all for a moment. For the soulless market, she well knew, did not spill out its jackpots on the basis of need—and she had too little money to risk making mistakes. Curiously, these people who already had it seemed in the happy position of begetting more, as if *their* dollars were peculiarly fertile. Or, as Jane imagined, the knowledge the rich could afford to pay for more rewarding than the free advice lying around on brokers' counters. The only question, really, was how to come by the proper information, and even Wally had said, "It takes patience." But now, perched on a hilltop with the wind in her hair, and with the stars above trying to outwink the lights below, Jane reveled in feeling her nearness to first and last things. Maybe the lyrical San Francisco night thus convinced her: prized knowledge was coming breathlessly close.

Interrupting her reverie, Wally grunted his pleasure, started the engine, and they sped downhill.

On the way Wally talked about Mrs. Hope. He had taken her to a movie the night before. "She's homesick for Dallas," he said. "She told me she'd go back except there's nothing to go back *to*." His lips twisted in sympathy.

Jane was touched by Wally's feeling for people. Most unusual, she thought, for a young man to care about the longings of women twice his age. Yes, Wally was gay, but he was kind and thoughtful too. She was so positive Eleanor would like him.

Reaching Jane's apartment, he was delighted to be invited in.

Eleanor was curled up in Horace's old chair with a copy of *Lady Chatterley's Lover*. When she heard the key in the front door below, she closed the book and carefully tucked it, title hidden, in the space at the side of the seat cushion. She got up hastily, smoothed her blouse, ran her thumbs around the waistband of her black velvet toreador pants and then sat down again with her legs under her in the position she'd finally decided, after considerable thought and practice, to adopt. She moistened her lips and gave her hair a final pat just as they arrived, seated demurely in the chair of poor Horace.

"Eleanor," said Jane, her hand on Wally's arm, "This is Mr. Googins—Wally—a classmate of mine."

Eleanor smiled at the classmate. The tone of Jane's telephone call had prepared her for something rather unusual—nothing, however, so startling as the blazing splendor of Wally's tattersall.

Wally was enchanted. The genius of special situations clearly regarded this as one. He turned to Jane. "You have permitted me to believe," he said reproachfully, "that you lived alone. Aunt Jane, this is a clear case of negligence—you could have introduced me to this lovely creature months ago."

"I do live alone. Except for Kimmy boy." She picked up Kim and Wally admired the handsome cat. "Now if you two will excuse me—." Jane headed toward her kitchen.

Wally pulled up an ottoman and sat at Eleanor's feet, letting the full impact of his charm fall upon her. His eye, not unnaturally, caught the book tucked in the seat by Eleanor's left hip.

"You've been reading a book," he said. "I hope you haven't damaged those lovely eyes. People can go blind from too much reading, you know. What is it?"

"Oh, it's just a tiresome old book on life adjustment. I have to keep ahead of my kindergartners."

Wally considered this a moment. "So you're a teacher. Do you have school tomorrow?"

"Tomorrow's Saturday—no, not tomorrow."

"Tomorrow, then, being Saturday—I take it that you are perfectly free to brawl, carouse, roister, raise hell generally?"

Eleanor's laugh tinkled through the apartment. "Oh, of course! You've just described my normal weekend."

"I was leading up to this—would you consider coming out to ride around the block in my snappy new car and maybe take on a chocolate malted milk—say with an egg in it?"

After giving him a precisely-calculated moment of doubt, Eleanor replied, "The egg really does it. I'd love to, but would it be polite—to leave Aunt Jane so soon?"

"Who's leaving so soon?" Jane came in bearing a tray with coffee equipment.

"Wally wants to take me around the block in his new car."

"That would hardly seem worth the trouble."

"I know a pretty big block," Wally assured her.

"Go on, Eleanor. The car is delightful. I'll take this coffee over to Al and Rosie so it won't be wasted."

As soon as they left Jane tore down the hall to the Bonelli apartment.

"Eleanor and Wally are out this very minute in his new car!" she announced.

"Wonderful!" Rosemarie, having seen neither young man, had long favored Wally over Petry. "I just know she'll like him."

Al was lighting his pipe and blowing up a cloud of smoke. Jane's news had no visible lifting effect on him.

"Al," Jane said. "Didn't you hear? Eleanor's out with Wally in his new car."

"What kinda car?"

"Good Heavens! Does that matter? It's a Triumph sports car."

"That's good." He sat down glumly. "At least," he said after a heavy silence, "it's got bucket seats, and bucket seats are the greatest impediment to hanky-panky since the bundling board."

"Al Bonelli—watch your imagination," said Rosemarie.

"I'm just trying to be practical. But the thing is that I don't like this Wally jerk being out with our Eleanor. Everything I've heard about him makes him sound like a tin-horn con artist. *I'm* going to wait up till she gets home. I got some questions to ask her."

"You'll do no such thing," said Rosemarie.

"Let's *all* stay up," Jane suggested brightly.

At one-thirty, with Eleanor still not back, they gave up waiting and Jane went home to bed.

# EIGHT

~~~~~~~~~~~~~~~~~~~~~~~~~~~~~~~~~~~~~~~~~~~

M r. Petry, who was redundant about few things, repeatedly told his girls, "Unless you *know* your broker personally, don't let him tell you what to buy. You tell him." On this subject, in fact, the teacher brimmed over with imperatives. "Nine hundred and ninety-nine out of a thousand brokers are conscientious and experienced men of good will," he said, leaving his fraternity wide and honorable quarter. Jane listened carefully, gathered that it is this thousandth character who has dogs and cats to get rid of, or who "churns and twists" his clients. She hadn't known what such painful-sounding verbs meant until Mr. Petry gave a few horrible examples of brokers' senseless trading in and out to add to their commissions.

So seldom was Mr. Petry given to such forcefulness that Jane couldn't cope with it. Her notebook meekly recorded, "You tell broker. Unless he's your husband, don't listen."

Mrs. Hope whispered to Jane, "My Mr. Evans is a doll. He calls me every day."

Mr. Petry didn't know it, and Jane had promised not to tell, but her teammate still traded like mad all the time, for kicks. Now, handing over a record book, she showed Jane how she had been in and out of fifteen stocks during the last three weeks. Since Mrs. Hope had a total of twenty-two, her list could not be considered dusty.

"Look," she nudged, as with one finger she underlined her latest transaction, "Mr. Evans took me in and out of this in two days!"

Vasiliu

Jane looked, saw the story on Texas Hot Air Generators. "I couldn't resist the name of Texas!" Mrs. Hope said. She had purchased 700 shares and had sold the whole works the next day. Her profit was $10.88, while Mr. Evans' was $149.66.

Another, Tarzan Timber, Mrs. Hope bought and held three days. It gave her a nice profit of $453.35—that is, if you didn't count Mr. Evans' commission of $82.59. And Mrs. Hope didn't. Her emotions were not equipped to deal with net figures. "Isn't it thrilling?" she gasped. "I *adore* taking a flyer!"

On a third transaction, Electric Eel, she took a loss of $189.71, by the side of Mr. Evans' gain of $81.04.

All told, while listening to Mr. Petry with one ear and Mrs. Hope with the other, Jane rapidly calculated that her madcap friend's last three flyers had netted her $274.52 and Mr. Evans $313.29, with his profit exceeding his client's by $38.77.

Jane could bear to see no more. She quietly closed Mrs. Hope's record book, and for her friend she prayed a silent prayer. Her teammate was behaving like a pressure cooker without a safety valve.

Somewhere between Mr. Petry's warning and Mrs. Hope's wheeling and dealing, Jane decided to take her stand. Apparently, selecting stocks was like being born and dying; it was something you had to do alone.

By this time, woefully confused by everybody else's method, she was ready to devise her own. As far as she knew, it was a wholly new way—and about time. It was at least refreshing, she thought, and it might even teach the cold canyon of Wall Street a thing or two about purely esthetic pleasure.

Sitting down at her card table the next morning, Jane had at it, with a wondrous sense of relief. Kim, jumping up to join her, curled himself on a sunny corner and, between naps, observed her with what she took to be approval. Occasionally he talked, as is the habit of Siamese cats—and Jane took eternal amusement—

as Horace had—from answering Kim with an endearment. Then he would happily flail his tail.

She began by grouping the letters of the alphabet into threes. Then she marked yellow work sheets "ABC," "DEF," and so on. But it was the next step—a crucial one—that showed her passion for perfection. For her entries into their proper alphabetical categories she fastidiously selected only those stocks whose names pleased her ear or kindled her sense of imagery. They had to do one or the other, and if they didn't, they were rejected like so many imposters. Not having heard much about individual stocks yet anyway, this new selection technique provided a thrilling experience in matching gossamer fantasy against harsh corporate reality. And Jane was a whiz at imagery.

On the "ABC" page, dismissing American Hoist and Derrick as esthetically impossible, she finally selected American Marietta and then smiled her satisfaction. "Marietta" sounded like Miss America of the old-fashioned South and brought to mind pictures of glistening magnolias and frosty mint juleps. In fact, Jane could all but hear the darkeys' banjos a-strummin', and for all she knew about American Marietta at that point, it could well have manufactured banjos.

Scrutinizing the B's one by one, she had to pass them over completely. Baldwin-Lima, Bangor and Aroostook, Bath Iron, Bendix Aviation, Bridgeport Brass, Buckeye Pipe Line—all brought images of ponderous tonnage and shrill noise. How, Jane wondered, did the tender name of Bethlehem ever get mixed up with steel?

The C's were more rewarding—especially Cascade Plywood, which sounded rippling, snowcapped, eternal. It lifted her spirits. She reached out to stroke Kim's chocolate-colored ears, and set off his purring machine.

Several categories left her down, but none more sharply than "JKL." It contained, of course, the tempting name of "Lone Star," and Jane knew exactly how Mrs. Hope would feel. Radiant in the vast skydome of Texas, "Lone Star" was something she could tie both heartstrings and pursestrings to, in part because of her teammate's nostalgia. But not when the lovely name was weighted by such crass suffixes as "Oil" and "Cement." Surely there was something better for "Lone Star." And so, as she thoughtfully marked her way through the alphabet, Jane found her soft goods spirit at odds with a hard goods age.

Finally she had a preliminary list of 50 stocks that met her esthetic standard, which was basic, and now she could no longer evade the second question: What did these companies with the alluring names *do?* What's more, *how well* did they do?

Gingerly, like a little girl afraid to open her valentine for fear it might be a cruel comic, Jane picked up her Stock Guide for a look behind the quaint name, American Marietta. This romantic, magnolia-laden company of banjo-strummin' employees turned out to be, in reality, one of the nation's busiest manufacturers of paint, concrete pipe, and resins. But if Jane's gentle soul was dismayed, she was utterly crestfallen to find that the jolly name of Joy Manufacturing, which made her think of popcorn balls at Christmas, actually stood for mining machinery. Stiffening her lip, she saw what she was up against: The business world was simply insensitive to the alchemy of words.

Next came her final test, as rigorous as the first was gentle. *How* did her candidates do? For two days, holding out against the lines of fine print, she combed and tabulated earnings reports in her Stock Guide. It was a dull, miserable, patience-taxing job.

She knew what she wanted—growth stocks only—of the type Mr. Petry would call "too aggressive for a widow." No sober-sided slow-movers for Jane. She had to think Big.

Furthermore, any securities casually posing as growth stocks had to prove it—and no monkey business. Earnings had to show a history of growth like Jack's Beanstalk—which, as Wall Street figures time, Jane knew, would be at the rate of 25 to 50 per cent a year. Preferably faster.

Unfortunately, however, Jane's creaky arithmetic proved a serious embarrassment to her research. She had loved to read about certain companies' percentage increases over the years—but she had forgotten how to figure percentages for herself. And not to know how to calculate her candidates' increases over the past few years was like trying to judge cloth without feeling it, or paint without seeing it. Thus, feeling unutterably stupid, Jane's exercise in stock selection ground to a dead-end halt. Leaving her work table to make a cup of tea, she tried to be patient until Al got home from work. Surely Al could teach her what she had to know. Naturally, such ignorance was intolerable.

That evening, with his usual gusto, Al threw himself into the problem of teaching his old teacher—and to their mutual delight they found that Jane's arithmetic came back fast. She was ecstatic. Actually, the formula Al gave her was easy. She went home and practiced delightedly.

But the next evening, to her surprise, Al brought over a slide rule. He had borrowed it from the bank.

"This," he informed her, "will be even better. Not necessary, but fun." Al offered to buy her own at a nice discount.

"My percentage gains," she told him, "must take off vertically and wobble not at all. Show me how to use it."

By the end of an hour Jane was setting up her problems with confidence and also flipping off percentages on the slide rule, which proved to be a powerful and fascinating gadget. Like a small boy with a new hammer and a pocket full of nails, she wielded her new tool with cheerful abandon—calculating the percentage relationships between such factors as Dow-Jones averages *vs.* the number of letters in a corporation's name, carloadings *vs.* average rainfall, and the number of stockholders in a given corporation *vs.* hog arrivals in Omaha. Her feeling of power mounting, she sent off a subscription to *FORTUNE*.

Finally, she pared away unmercifully, her slide rule within easy reach, at her preliminary list of fifty stocks with acceptable names. Most of them simply flunked her flight test; they either hadn't got off the ground or, after a wobbly start, had squibbed out and, from her viewpoint, died. What they died of—TV advertising, strikes, competition, playboy presidents or senility on the board—she had no way of knowing or need to guess.

In a manner of speaking, she was selecting her stock in the same way she had selected a casaba melon at her grocer's that very week. Caught with a shipment of green melons, the grocer marked them down. "You ladies can let 'em ripen," he said. "I gotta have the space." Jane was perfectly delighted to let both melon and stock ripen in her space and on her time.

One stock survived, a stock so immature that it had not yet rated a grade of A, B, C or D in her Stock Guide. But it had burgeoned as if primed by Vigoro and watered by Pluvis. Actually, it was the handiwork of mere mortal men—who happened to be, in this case, a group of scientists with an eye for profits, for the future, and for exciting applications in fields not already plowed by competitors. And Jane, her screening done, collapsed into excited expectancy.

That night Rosemarie asked her over for a dinner of flank steak, which Jane had taught her to marinate in burgundy and Japanese soy sauce, and in telling about her stock selection at dinner, she couldn't contain her lyricism. Al and Rosemarie both said it sounded magnificent, in fact predestined.

During the next class hour she wrote the name of her stock on a slip of paper and handed it to Wally. "That," she whispered proudly, "is a *baby* blue chip."

Glancing at the name, Wally looked at her with low-grade tolerance. "Oh, you whimsical women." He added flatly, "I never heard of it."

During class break she went outside a few minutes with Wally to savor the lovely evening, but she couldn't get her stock out of her mind. "I am perfectly serious," she said. "What I've found is a baby blue chip. People are utterly obsessed by indigo-blue

blue chips. It's a kind of ancestor worship—with everything based on the past, not the future." She mentioned several venerable blue chips, out of steam, that were riding along on past reputation. "You can't be a snob about blood lines in this business," she went on, "If you . . ."

Wally interrupted.

"I am vibrating with interest. Do tell me more."

If he sounded impatient, he was—perhaps because of the date. It was on a day when every investor from San Francisco to New York was clammy and short-tempered with fear. On that day alone the value of common stocks dropped more than $5 billion.

But blessed is the faith of the serene and wholehearted. Jane knew about the bust, but considered it merely a boring interruption, as, when teaching, she had to put up with things like historical pageants. It didn't even register when the brooding Wally, back in class, wrote in a note, "You're a *foolish* Aunt Jane. We'll all be shorn neked as turkeys by Thanksgiving." She read the note smiled, and answered by writing an uppity quotation from Pliny. " 'The best plan is to profit by the folly of others.' Your kind of faith makes it much easier to profit."

Then her mind shot forward to that bright day, now six months hence, when Mr. Petry would compare all the students' projected gains and would single her out for the prize.

# *NINE*

~~~~~~~~~~~~~~~~~~~~~~~~~~~~~~~~~~~~~~~~~~

I t was Sunday morning and Eleanor, dropping in
to read Jane's *Chronicle,* announced she was driving up to Tomales Bay for a picnic lunch.

"Let me guess who you're going with!" Jane teased. In truth,
she couldn't guess whether it was Wally or Mr. Petry. Eleanor
acted happy—but with an indefinable lag.

"I'm all shook up," she finally said unsmiling. "It's Phil—
but I *think* I wish it were Wally! Isn't that terrible?"

Jane's heart set up such a tune she thought it would surely be
heard, and she made a mental note to tell Al and Rosemarie that
Eleanor had finally given her first sign of preference. Wally was
less attentive and would be much slower to educate to the idea of
settling down, which was undoubtedly a part of his attraction. But
time would be a mighty ally, and actually it was just as well to
give a free soul like Wally some stiff competition.

They heard the car horn and Eleanor jumped up and ran out
the door. In serene confidence that Eleanor would not, Jane called
after her, "Have a wonderful day, dear!" Then she hastened to
Al's and Rosemarie's to bring them up to date.

\*   \*   \*   \*   \*

Whenever an impulse struck Jane these days, it was as good as
executed—in part, perhaps, because she was alone and free to act.
Hardly anything could be worse. In Horace, Jane had enjoyed an
anchor, a judgment, a reflective thought. But with Jane an im-

pulse often meant reflex action—even if, occasionally it was delayed by rationalizing.

It was during her next class session that she was seized, so suddenly, she wondered why she had been content with her imaginary list and all this play acting. Why not take her enthusiastic choice to a broker and really put her money to doubling and tripling right away? What was she waiting for? True, Mr. Petry had requested his beginners not to invest until after they had finished his course. *Then,* he had reminded the ladies at least five times, he would be so happy to serve them himself. But Jane figured that her talent alone put her well ahead of schedule. She was not a beginner after all, but a seasoned investor. Thus persuaded, the longer she thought of her $9000, plus the little money she had in addition, the more reckless it seemed to neglect investing it any longer.

With rare insight, she now smiled at her own artifice. Not until a solution had presented itself, she noted, had she dared realize how frightened and alone she was. But thank Heaven, she thought, our economic society—which makes no room for women of my age—needs and wants our money, and may even pay handsomely for it. Jane smiled as she thought of Wally's name for women in the market—"mudhens." And he had said admiringly, "Some mudhens are really terrific." Being seized, she couldn't wait to begin, and during class break, when the two walked half a block and back, for fresh air, she confided her impulse to Wally. Quoting Benjamin Franklin, she said loftily, "Wally, 'the investment that pays the most interest is your own knowledge'."

Wally mumbled a faint "Yeah?" Clearly she had not intrigued him.

"Tomorrow I start buying a slice of industrial America," she went on. "Private investment is the romance of production, the yeast of the future, the life blood of our economy."

"You are," Wally said cruelly, "getting your metaphors mixed."

This was better. He was at least listening. Now she was ready. "Tomorrow morning," she lowered her voice, "I am putting $10,000 into transistors, magnetic . . ."

Jane never got any farther. Wally choked on his cigarette. Recovered, he turned to stare at his walking companion as if seeing her for the first time, and then he flashed a winning smile. She was chic and she did have a soft voice and a certain naivete that was appealing as a lilac is appealing.

"You are," he said brightly, "more beautiful than brilliant. A full-blown depression roaring in and every sane person burying his money in a sock. But *you* choose this moment to invest."

A little hurt by his vehemence, Jane stoutly defended herself. "You are," she said, "very unimaginative. You have never really learned how and when to shop. The time to buy furs is when nobody wants them—in May."

Observing her firmness of chin and voice, Wally judged she meant to do precisely when she said. Not quite ready for this challenge, but rising above a certain tug at his conscience, he decided to introduce her to one of his "Special Situations." It was Canadian Countess, a company underwritten by his own firm and a "surefire bonanza" in petrochemicals. Wally was just launching into an ecstatic description when it was time to run back to Mr. Petry.

In class again, Wally scribbled in the back of Jane's notebook, "It's in Peace River country. Stuning operation with 100 employees all ready. Venture financed in part by Osgood Allen, Canadian oil millionair. Stock now 25¢ per share. Will be 50¢ by first of year, one dollar by next summer. Yours for the Countess."

Jane wrote back, "Why do you say this is going up if everything else is going down?"

Wally hesitated, but not perceptibly, and scribbled back "Special Situation," as if this explained everything. Then he added,

"We control. Osgood Allen ready to buy any number shares $2 per. But we want to keep control in family. Won't let Os have too many."

Puzzled by the excited scribbling of her seatmates, Mrs. Hope passed Jane a note saying, "Don't buy the Golden Gate without letting me in on it." Jane patted her arm and laughed.

After class that night, Wally walked Jane down Van Ness to Tommy's Joynt. Jane, thrilled to see the inside of a popular bistro she knew only through Herb Caen's column, suddenly felt destined for more night life—and adored the sensation. Sitting at a red-and-white checked table near a big column, Jane looked around while Wally ordered.

"Two Irish Coffees," he decided. "Be sure it's O'Flaherty's Whiskey." Then he excused himself to go speak with a friend he saw sitting at the bar.

A soft tango began coming from grills in the walls, and Jane's sense of joy, always close to the surface, bobbed up and unfolded like a morning glory to the sun. To the eye, Tommy's Joynt looked like a hilarious grab-bag of relics dating from the 1890's— including stained-glass lamp shades and dusty German beer ads featuring ladies considerably heftier than the contemporary Miss Rhinegolds. Nailed high to one wall, for no reason Jane could guess, hung an old deep sea diver's outfit and, next to it, magnificent murals depicted the horrors of the 1906 San Francisco earthquake and fire. A sign underneath the murals read cooly, "Please remain seated while room is in motion." She pointed it out to Wally.

Sitting down opposite her, he grinned and pointed to his favorite sign, hanging over the bar. "If you're so damn smart, why ain't you rich?" In her present dilemma, the sentiment struck Jane as more sensible than funny.

"Being poor," she said flatly, "is the biggest boredom of all. It is so *daily*, so ungenerous, so monotonous. One never has anything new, like this." The music had changed to a charming waltz.

"I can say these things finally, I suppose, because—well, because they'll soon be behind me!" The prospect flooded her emotions and she went on talking about the indignities of the little things— of foraging and scrimping in mean little ways that eroded; at the dull things—like cheap stockings in a supermarket, magazines read in a stiff library chair, cheap meats that had to be cooked slowly. Scores of such daily compromises, all on the down side, trooped through her mind.

"Well," said Wally, signalling for another Irish Coffee, "if you're really smart, that beautiful Canadian Countess can make you rich. Stock is tightly held, but for you I could manage."

"Could you?" Jane's breath quickened. "Oh, how wonderful, Wally."

"We'll just make you part of the firm's family," Wally said. "But you must keep this off the record. If this ever got back to old Petry, he'd try grabbing the Countess for his own firm."

Jane couldn't imagine anybody's being so greedy, but men were sometimes peculiar. She agreed not to breathe a word.

Wally grinned, "Not a peep to the girls either, huh? Or to Eleanor. She might forget and let something slip. This is strictly between us."

Jane was sorry about Eleanor, but maybe later. . . .

"How can I," she asked with emotion, "ever repay you for such kindnesses?"

"Tell Eleanor I'm great stuff." Wally grinned. Feeling expansive, he ordered still another round and chortled, "This is like getting into AT and T around 1912 at three cents a share."

While he talked on, Jane settled back to enjoy the gay atmosphere, which soon gave way to competition in a spate of her own spectacular imagery. The wondrous beauty of western Canada she had read about, and the delightful name of Canadian Countess was somehow the crowning touch. If Horace and she had never had the money to travel and to visit Canada, she reflected how pleasant it was that their dollars could.

Now she told Wally of the gay times she and Horace used to have in the spring, collecting travel folders and asking all their friends for tips on resorts. "You'd be amazed," she said, smiling, "how many countries we visited, how many oceans we sailed!"

Wally nodded. "Most of the fun lies in the planning part anyway."

"Yes," said Jane. "We never got farther than Berkeley."

Not until the two of them were leaving did they notice the bold sign just above their heads on the column beside their table. "A fool and his money are soon parted," it read. "Who got yours?"

Jane smiled. "Cute, isn't it?"

"Yeah," said Wally. "Yeah."

# TEN

~~~~~~~~~~~~~~~~~~~~~~~~~~~~~~~~~~~~~~~~~~~

Setting out the next morning for her first investment venture in Montgomery Street, Jane car-
ried Mr. Petry's advice about unfamiliar brokers high in her
mind: "You tell him what to buy." Wally, of course, was different. Bless him, he was a friend welcoming her into the family.
Jane wondered hopefully whether she would ever again purchase
such a dazzling prospect. She had written Wally a check for
$3000, with just one niggling regret. Wally couldn't yet trust
even Eleanor. But, of course, if he and Eleanor kept on counting
daisies together . . .

Striding along down the Bush Street hill, Jane smiled to herself
so broadly that perfectly strange passers-by smiled back, and a
sidewalk photographer took her for a tourist. She was thinking
of Wally's jealousy, which made him behave peculiarly and by
turns supplicating and demanding. Eleanor was, after all, still
seeing Mr. Petry every night he was not teaching, which also
happened to be Wally's only free nights. And *he*, bad boy that
he was, had taken to cutting classes just in order to beat Phil's
time.

It was all too delicious for Jane, especially since Eleanor was
in that enviable state of liking both suitors and of being dramatically torn. Rosemarie felt a little tearful about it, while Al
damned women for being double-crossers. But Jane looked upon
the whole thing as a rich, maturing, euphoric experience due
every woman at least once. Anything that built sentimental
memories for one's later years was all to the good.

Just last week, on Eleanor's twenty-second birthday, Jane and Rosemarie had thought it so cute when Wally tied one lovely white rose to a polished apple and addressed it "to my teacher." Now that was the kind of thing one could file under Fond Memories. And Phil Petry? He had given her Caron's *Fleurs de Rocaille*. Charming, yes, and expensive! But Jane noticed that Eleanor had proudly put the apple on her bedside table.

Oh, well, thought Jane, whatever little Eleanor finally decided, *she* was not taking any sides. It wouldn't be fair. The child had to live her own life. As Jane approached the financial district, her thoughts went back to her own problems.

About her second stock purchase in less than twenty-four hours, she had no question whatever. Her own special selection "JKL," had all sorts of eye and ear appeal, its growth had shown the required degree of hyperthyroidism and, what's more, its business stirred her vision of tomorrow. It was the dream of the future that excited Jane, not the timid reality of today. With science soaring upward to probe the galaxy of which Earth was only a speck, and diving downward to probe the cozy, inky, bottomless deep of the oceans, Jane was easily seized with a sense of orbital destiny. "Now," had written Carl Sandburg, "man has taken the ball of earth and made it a little thing." Whatever man was doing crawling around on the ocean floors did not register clearly with Jane, possibly because inky blackness does not invite mental imagery. But the heavens above her head were already busy with men hawking their wares from shiny platforms and corresponding with each other by means of a sort of luminous, celestial Pony Express.

Let Wally indulge his jitters, she thought as she turned into Montgomery Street. She had no patience with pessimism. The faint of heart simply lacked 20-20 vision. Moreover, since none of the boardroom oracles agreed on anything anyway, it made sense to think in terms of the era as a whole, and of its *individual* performers. Well, from her trio of "J K L," she had finally chosen hers.

She stopped in at the Hocum and Pullem Investment Company because there she could not only buy her stock but could also see a stunning electronics quotation board. With boyish envy Mr. Petry had described this miracle, which he was proud to say Sharp and Blarney was also installing, and it suited her mood to a T. Standing gaping at the huge black and red mural with its bright white figures clicking like hundreds of telegraph keys, Jane could scarcely contain her feeling of exaltation. The white figures, she knew—and it was almost too much—clicked out the instantaneous news of prices being paid for stock in every corner of the country—even before investors had left their brokers' desks. With such a fantastic world offering a paradise of assurance, Jane began to be aware of a curious emotion suffusing the innermost core of her body. It was, she realized, a wonderful new feeling of belonging, of sharing, of going somewhere. Instinctively, she smiled at a couple of women who were sitting down watching the board. They nodded cordially.

What a contrast to the aloneness she felt in her supermarket! There alongside other women, she could never escape the chill of her single-status purchases—one can of soup, one quart of milk, one grapefruit. Lining up at the cashier's counter Jane always found herself between customers whose carts were loaded with half-gallons of milk, soup cans by the dozen, and grapefruit by the netted bag: to lone women, the supermarket's most wicked reproach was the grocery cart itself. It had become a perambulator. No matter how gently Jane pushed her cart, the thing always clattered open, always spread its tot's seat wide—and always lanced her heart.

But this *new* feeling of belonging—this too was basic, almost as basic as a supermarket—also carried daily meaning. Actually, she reflected with a sudden start of joy, she now even belonged to a "family!"

She was still mulling over such comforting thoughts when a bright-eyed, wire-haired young man across the room caught her eye. Smiling hopefully, he freed himself from a small group of mourners—the market was a graveyard that day—and bounded over to her. Over-enthusiastically, he introduced himself as Mr. Kilgore and talked about the morning fog as he escorted her down a narrow hall to his office. The fog was not dense enough to merit all the energy he gave it.

His office was the size of a small pony stall and, once they had settled down, Jane found herself uncomfortable with the ashtray under her nose and her knees hard against the desk. Now, in the place where decisions had to be faced, how cold things suddenly seemed! Jane was dismayed that brokerage firms—of all places—were so careless about putting customers at their ease. A broker's office ought to be cheerful, not chilly and cramped. Mr. Kilgore's pink manicure did not reassure her.

"Now!" he exclaimed. "What's on the little lady's mind?"

The little lady, wincing slightly, said she would like to make a purchase, and handed over a sheet of paper. "This is a baby blue chip," she smiled. "I want to buy 200 shares."

Mr. Kilgore looked at the name of the stock, consulted his Stock Guide, eyed her with noble pity, and then slowly shook his head.

"I would be most reluctant," he began, "most reluctant. Especially during these trying days." He paused, floundering, finally asked, "May I inquire what you are in now?"

Nettled, Jane couldn't resist. "Until recently, Longfellow Leasing. I sold at the top." Pausing to enjoy the effect of her astuteness, she went on gaily, "Right now I'm in Canadian Countess." The effect of *this* fell flat.

Mr. Kilgore looked shamefaced. "I never heard of it."

Brushing aside the possibility that he must not get around much, Jane explained, "It is comparable to buying American

Telephone in 1912 at three cents a share." Then she added, "But it's in the family, so to speak."

"Oh, hard to come by," Mr. Kilgore supplied, and dismissed the Countess as privately held and pretty smart. Then he pressed on. "Let me tell you about a little over-the-counter beauty." Writing "Bide-a-Wee Hotels" on a pad of paper, as if sharing a secret, he confided, "I put my mother in this only last week. It's slow growth, but steady and safe."

"I can't afford slow growers." Jane went on to explain that she was accustomed to doubling and tripling the value of her purchases—usually within a few months.

Mr. Kilgore appeared to be dashed, she noticed, but that was perhaps because he was young. After all, what she said was true enough. She didn't have a lifetime ahead of her for leisurely growth, and stocks as fast as Canadian Countess would have to be her answer. Nevertheless she assured Mr. Kilgore, "I don't want to seem unreasonable."

He feebly muttered, "Yes, yes, of course," and hung on to his desk as if to stop its swaying before his eyes.

Since he was obviously unappreciative, Jane could do little but promise to think about Bide-a-Wee Hotels and take her leave. But he was nice, if naive, and she felt sorry to have no business for him.

Going three doors down the street to another firm, she met a breezy young customer's man named Mr. Gaylord. His office, too, was in a row of tiny stalls but, even so, he talked loudly enough to command an auditorium. Taking one look at Jane's proposed purchase, Mr. Gaylord's Adam's apple bobbed over his blue bow tie. "Yipes!" he boomed. "You *are* a speculator, aren't you?"

Jane softly quoted Webster. " 'To speculate is merely to think about.' "

Jarring her with his decibels, Mr. Gaylord shouted on, introduced the idea of mutual funds as "wonderful for one in your position"—not that *he* knew what that was.

In mentioning the mutual funds, Mr. Gaylord had touched a quivering nerve. For no class lesson on any subject had buoyed Jane's hope so high, nor dashed it so low.

In the beginning, as Mr. Petry had explained the mutuals, the idea of buying shares in mighty investment trusts, which in turn invested one's money in the market, had appealed to Jane as a simply heroic concept. Especially because they provided professional management. She could practically *see* the experienced managers in action—beatific financial wizards huddled around a conference table, sifting esoteric knowledge, weighing shrewd decisions, and finally toting up one bonanza after another for their little investors. No wonder the whole country had become mutual-fund happy! In fact, Mr. Petry had called the mutual funds "the poor man's investment counsellor," and for the financial wizards to feel such altruism had touched her deeply.

But the more Mr. Petry had talked, the sharper had become her notes on two aspects of the mutual funds—the actual results they achieved for their investors and the fee usually charged them for joining. The whole idea seemed to be about as exciting as an envelope tucked under the mattress.

Now that Mr. Gaylord had brought up the subject, however, Jane wanted to refresh her memory, and she fished in her purse for her notebook. Excusing herself, she flipped the pages and read silently. "Put $10,000 into American Something-or-Other today and tomorrow what do you have? $9200. Not me! Can't afford such high initiation fee. Better trust self."

Sweetly, she now pointed out to Mr. Gaylord, "I can buy my single stock for much less commission. And of course it will do far better."

Mr. Gaylord raised an eyebrow and persisted, "But a mutual gives you diversification."

Jane gave him her nicest smile. She didn't bother to tell Mr. Gaylord, but her notebook also said, "Diversification is a sacred cow."

Making no headway with the mutuals, Mr. Gaylord next tried the utilities. "They are depression proof," he said. "I put my mother-in-law in Puget Sound only last week."

Jane only hoped Puget Sound was the name of a utility. Promising Mr. Gaylord to think about utilities, and taking her leave, she reflected that her maiden visits with brokers were teaching her at least one thing: she appealed to their filial instincts. Sentimentally, she wondered if Wally had been thoughtful enough to put his mother in Canadian Countess.

The next customer's man from whom she tried to buy, in a firm across the street, reminded her of a beatnik—off-the-premises, to be sure.

He hooted, "Two hundred shares! You don't really feel earth-bound a-tall, do you. You just don't care *what* happens." With a delicious afterthought, he laughed, "I wouldn't sell that to my own mother."

Jane left hastily, but not before he had pressed a prospectus into her hand.

"Now this stock," he said, "is a real gasser."

Jane dropped the prospectus in the first corner trash can she passed.

Seeing the smartly tailored matron helping to keep San Francisco's streets clean, the handsome, white-gloved traffic officer at the intersection shot her a dazzling smile and even blew her a short whistle.

# *ELEVEN*

~~~~~~~~~~~~~~~~~~~~~~~~~~~~~~~~~~~~

L ate one Thursday morning the mailman rang and handed Jane a bulky brown envelope with 21 cents postage due. It contained her certificates of the Canadian Countess Petrochemicals Company. Considering what they represented, they were, to her dismay, folded much too carelessly. She removed them tenderly while admiring their handsome red borders, their Old English print, and their illegible signatures. Bringing out the ironing board, she ironed out the creases under a damp cloth, then rolled them into slender cylinders. Finally, rummaging among her old Christmas wrappings and ribbons, saved from year to year in a lower kitchen drawer, she tied a slender red ribbon around each certificate. There were forty-eight in all, each one representing 250 shares of a grand total of 12,000 shares, and stacked on the kitchen table they made an awesome pyramid of assets.

Taking three empty one-pound coffee cans—she saved these for her home painting projects—she stood her 48 certificates upright in the cans and put them high on a pantry shelf. There, behind a cupboard door, they would be safe and out of sight. Three or four times during the next few minutes, after she had shut the door upon them, she couldn't resist opening it again to look at her investment of $3000 and realize anew what the handsome certificates meant to her security.

Her mood of exaltation soon sagged, however, to give way to an aching desire to share her secret with Al and Rosemarie.

Vasiliu

Nothing was any fun unless it was shared. Why, oh why, she thought impatiently, had Wally been so insistent upon keeping such a spectacular fortune secret?

For one sixty-second minute Jane remained torn in indecision. Should she or shouldn't she tell them? Then a perfectly splendid rationalization came to mind. She owed it to her safety to show Al and Rosemarie exactly where she kept her mounting assets. What if she were suddenly taken to a hospital? There could be a fire or an earthquake! Who would know to rescue her certificates? And what if she *died* in the hospital? Then big headlines would appear in all the papers: WEALTHY WIDOW LIVED MODESTLY. It was morally wrong not to trust one's friends.

In a spirit of emergency, and with the feeling of just beating the ambulance, Jane turned to bang on the kitchen wall, and her thumps quickly brought both Al and Rosemarie. Since it was Thursday morning, and their morning off, they were puttering around in their jeans.

Without a word Jane reached up for the coffee cans and one by one lined them up on the kitchen table. The beribboned certificates, five inches taller than their containers, looked like unclaimed diplomas. Trying to figure out the display, not to mention Jane's expression, Al blurted, "What goes on? You running a diploma mill?"

Jane had the sudden feeling that Al made her act more theatrical than other people did, and she began to explain Wally's "special situation" with gestures intended to represent petrochemicals. She ended proudly, "Canadian Countess will turn me into a dowager with a lorgnette. I shall have wall-to-wall carpeting. I shall *insist* upon Irish Coffee at breakfast!"

Rosemarie, silently going after first things first, was counting the certificates, can by can. "How many should you have?" she asked.

"Forty-eight," said Jane. "Sixteen per can."

"I get forty-seven." Rosemarie started counting again, and the second time she got forty-nine. But she averaged out and was content. She opened a certificate and held it for Al to see.

"Jane," said Al, "You know there's nothing in life I'd rather see than you make a killing."

Recognizing the preface to a heavy moral, Jane sighed. It came right away.

"But for the love of God, do you know what you're doing? My boss says penny stocks are the biggest fraud that's ever been perpetrated upon a helpless people. If you . . ."

Jane interrupted, "Yes, yes, I know. But this time I bought a broker instead of a stock." She had not thought of it that way until she heard herself saying it, and she liked what she'd said. It was *good*. Somewhere in her reading she had picked up an old Chinese proverb, and recalled it just in time. "If you can't know the merchandise, know the merchant."

Lighting his pipe, Al looked up. "I'll take care of that Wally personally." He grinned. "If he does anything to hurt you, I'll swab the decks with 'im."

Since Rosemarie had left soup on her stove, she hurried on back home. But Al stayed long enough to tell Jane something he had been burning to tell her for two days. Her lavish show of certificates now made things just right.

"Rosie doesn't know it yet," he whispered, leaning close, "I want to surprise her. But I dug up enough cash to get ten shares of your A Number One Choice U. S. Inspected stock! I bought day before yesterday and it's already up fifty cents! I've already made five dollars!"

He and Jane fell into each other's arms and tried to stifle their yelps of delight.

"But you rouge, you monster!" Jane came to. "You beat me to it. I can't find a broker who'll let me buy it!"

"You went to the wrong places. My man knew it. Even thought I must be smart."

Thus early Monday morning, shortly after the market had

opened, Jane was sitting across the desk from Al's broker, a Mr. Blassingame. She tried to order her stock, but Mr. Blassingame wouldn't be rushed. He was a plump, placid, middle-aged man who fingered his ear lobe and asked her lots of unexpected questions. Finally, he told her, "Yes, I recall Mr. Albert Bonelli and his purchase very well indeed. But his circumstances are somewhat different from yours. He is a businessman. You are a widow. You do not have regular employment." Mr. Blassingame tapped a pencil against his telephone and pondered.

"You say," he went on, "you own no life insurance, no property. Then you do have a savings account?"

"A small one," Jane wondered angrily whether this sadist was trying to make her burst into tears. She had the wild impulse to say, "But I do have a Siamese cat."

Jane knew it was coming. It did.

"I would say that the ideal investment for a widow in your situation is a mutual fund. Now United States Investors has fine diversification, and some of the smartest managers in the business." Mr. Blassingame reached in the drawer for a prospectus.

Jane felt her body becoming rigid. "What"—she tried to keep her voice even—"is the initiation fee?"

Mr. Blassingame laughed. "Well," he said. "Well!" He looked it up. "Eight and a half per cent."

.."So," said Jane, and she thought this enough for the moment. A vision ran through her head of massive mutual funds rising and falling with the market tides—with about as much maneuverability as a ship run aground in a mud-bank. And showing just as much promise of high sailing.

"This," Mr. Blassingame pressed the prospectus into her hands, "is the answer."

"There is a wonderful place for mutual funds," Jane waved her hand to encompass a fair share of the world, but a stubborn line formed between her eyes. "With investors who don't read or won't read, and they are many. I know them. I'm a teacher." Too, she thought but didn't mention it, they were fine for people who lived at sea, or in the desert, or marooned on mountain tops, and couldn't find out anything for themselves. Other excellent candidates for the mutual funds trotted through her mind, but they saddened her and she didn't mention them either—investors who were blind, deaf, or infirm.

When she walked out of Mr. Blassingame's office she was nearer to tears of frustration than she was to her purchase of her favorite stock.

* * * * *

If Jane turned out to be an unorthodox investor in unorthodox times, it was because she was, she eventually decided, firmly against Wall Street doctrine, which seemed to operate like a conditioned reflex. What's more, it was outmoded as a surrey and ferociously entrenched. Not a single adviser she had met had used any imagination about the special problems, the special needs, that the state of widowhood itself implied.

Nevertheless she had learned much—in reverse, that is—from young customer's men and from Mr. Petry. As he taught stock market strategy, she had, with rare sensitivity, extracted extraordinary lessons from strictly between the lines. In brief, her most important gleaning would have laid out young Phil Petry cold. But this is it, straight out of Jane's notebook:

"The individual with the least amount of money, and who therefore needs money most, is the one who gets the least expert help. She is the one who gets offered widow and orphan stocks or mutual funds. Thus she, of all investors, has least chance."

This observation bothered her so profoundly that she finally brought it up for class discussion. Mindful of her teacher's role, she tried to be tactful. After all, she herself, as a teacher, knew there had to be a lot of lip service to the conventions. Thus she put her question obliquely.

"Would you please explain the difference," she asked, "between a customer's man and an investment counsellor?"

The minute the question was out she knew there wasn't enough tact in the world to contain it. It was like asking a public school man to describe a private school, a clerk at Macy's to describe I. Magnin's, or a Texan to describe an Alaskan. Being polite, Mr. Petry indulged in a few moments of bland bumbling and wound up saying nothing—beyond the fact that a customer's man preferred to be called "a registered representative" or "an account executive."

Sensing what Jane was trying to get at, and delighted to see his rival's discomfort, Wally chimed in and pressed the question. "If you want to invest a hundred thousand," he said, "you can rate the services of an investment counsellor. Right?" Jane was glad Wally was there that night. Eleanor was at a PTA meeting.

Mr. Petry's ghostly smile had turned into a grimace. "Well, now."

Wally plunged on. "But if you have only a thousand bucks, you don't get beyond the customer's man. Okay?"

Mr. Petry began to protest. "The investment counsellor is more —well, he goes in for programming the individual account."

"Yeah," Wally grunted. "But you've got to have a tidy pile of dough before you can rate all that attention."

Jane kicked Wally's foot. There was no point in badgering poor Phil Petry, who was doing his level best to help people help themselves. She devoutly wished she had never brought up the question. A lot of people couldn't afford custom-tailored suits, either. Or psychoanalysis.

Meantime, this exchange had stirred up Mrs. Hope, who had never before heard of an investment counsellor. She whispered hurriedly, "You mean I can have a really special personal counsellor? If I have a hundred thousand dollars?"

Jane whispered back, "Yes. But you'd better hurry!"

Mrs. Hope, ecstatic to realize her new possibilities, couldn't wait to be faithless to her Mr. Evans.

Resolving the whole question in terms of her own resources,

Jane jotted down her next between-the-lines lesson in the conventions of investing. It was stated with classical simplicity: "The timid and the poor are to remain the timid and the poor. Only the rich are to become richer."

So much for the principles of wholesale advice—available in the stalls of any brokerage firm's front office. What Aunt Jane was after was tailor-made help.

Considering the way the market had plummeted, conscientious customer's men made it next to impossible for her to buy. At least what *she* wanted. Thinking over her feckless attempts with some amusement, she gathered that most brokers would lump her in a class with the American in Paris who simply hands over his wallet for a shop-keeper to make change. Maybe because she was a woman. Anyhow, Al had said he had bought without any question at all, and was astonished at Jane's experiences.

Now, however, she was wasting time. She would just have to be determined with the next broker, and this time she would choose him carefully in advance—preferably an older man who wouldn't think of Mother's Day the minute she walked in. Next, he had to be a specialist. Jane had no disposition to be critical of customer's men—but she did feel put out about so much advice, especially when it was unsolicited. During the last eight-day period, she noticed, Bide-a-Wee Hotels had lost a dollar. Puget Sound remained the same, and most mutuals, as usual, were ponderously going up two cents one day, and down two cents the next. Meanwhile, as she calculated, her inability to buy her favorite stock had already cost her $400. What was needed was action.

A day or so later, after considerable cogitation, Jane foresook the cold pony stalls and, late one afternoon, entered one of San Francisco's most distinguished investment counselling firms. There she calmly asked to see its head, a Mr. August Ernst. The receptionist smiled, invited her to be seated.

It was Mr. Ernst's late wife who had served on the school

board and exhibited such non-conformist views that Jane had admired so extravagantly. Also, aside from this tie, which gave her courage, she had seen Mr. Ernst's grey-thatched, kindly picture many times in the local press. With a mildly offbeat philanthropic bent, he had given his city much—a paid-up diaper service for its unwed mothers, a free beanery for its Skid Row, and a mandrill for its zoo. A man with such feeling for all forms and kinds of life, she felt, would surely understand her point of view.

He was also, of course, a brilliant financier. Now if *he* looked horrorstruck at her selection, she would swallow all her uncharitable thoughts about brokers and start her search all over again—a thought so black that it filled her with apprehension. Suddenly an icy impulse lifted her out of her chair, and all that saved a hasty exit through the door was the sweet-faced receptionist's questions about the weather. These required an answer, and one could not be rude.

But for the first time a monstrous understanding entered Jane's mind: in a field as foreign as prehistoric hieroglyphics, where even the specialists faltered, *she had dared presume both to find fault with existing precepts and to form her own opinion.* No doubt all those young men had been simply trying to save her from herself. How bumptious, how arrogant, how idiotic, she asked herself, had she been? Her confidence completely shattered, she jumped when a bell tinkled, and the receptionist smiled. "Mr. Ernst can see you now." Panicked, Jane thought of blurting, "Oh, I just wanted to see about magazine subscriptions. You can answer as well as he." But the receptionist was already leading her into an oak-panelled office where a handsome grey-haired, pink-cheeked man was awaiting her with some curiosity.

Once seated in a leather chair to the side of his desk, Jane paled visibly. How could she presume to take up the time of so important a man? Her breath caught at what she had done. Then it happened: as much to spare his feelings as her own, Jane's accommodating nature came to the rescue of both of them. Her imagination triggered her tongue and she began working on a heavy, heavy editing job.

"I am," she introduced herself, "the widow of a New York investment counsellor." Well, what could be more natural? After all, Mr. Gresham had once sent Horace as far as Chicago on a bookkeeping chore. Once this hurdle was taken, her momentum began coming up fast. "Horace always said," she went on, "the smart time to buy furs is in May." Well, he *could* very well have said that. Jane spoke with deep conviction. In fact, she could practically hear Horace. "And certainly this seems to be an off-season for the market."

Mr. Ernst nodded assent. But he said with confidence, "You know, I personally like this quiet kind of market. It's merely resting. It gives investors time to relax, to meditate, to be selective."

Delighted with an expression of such calm, Jane's panic disappeared. Mr. Ernst, turning to a mahogany cabinet, offered port wine, poured two. Under the influence of such fraternity with the widow of a colleague, he smiled convivially, and Jane heard herself volunteer, with becoming modesty, "My husband did very nicely, really, following his own advice to others."

Mr. Ernst pleasantly acknowledged, "Some of us do manage. We can get first-hand information."

"My husband also urged, 'Concentrate on specific situations rather than stock movements'." Not even sure she had her idioms right, Jane felt as daring as a foreigner testing his English. To try such a hard-won conclusion of her own on such an experienced expert might make her—or rather, Horace—sound silly.

To her delight, however, Mr. Ernst eyed her appreciatively and fairly shouted, "Bravo. You have no idea how nauseous it gets, day after day, hour after hour"—he pounded on his desk with passion—"to be asked to outguess the market." He mimicked, "'How is the market today?' 'Tell me what to expect of General Space Suit.' You'd think we all read tea leaves. The only thing to do at any time, fair or foul, is to get with brilliant management and stay put." Mr. Ernst's eyes were kind and knowing.

Excited to be so encouraged, Jane ran on, "I am so fully invested that I have only change at the moment." At this point, tugging briefly at her I. Magnin hat for reassurance, she handed Mr. Ernst the name of her stock. This was the moment of truth: upon his reaction she would stand or fall. And although she had worked herself up to it, she could scarcely bear the suspense of awaiting his reply.

"*Where*," he asked, eyeing her keenly, "did you come by this?"

That didn't mean anything, she told herself quickly. It was neither approval or disapproval.

"Oh," she smiled, fumbling. "Right now I almost feel I dreamed it."

Mr. Ernst laughed, thought her remark lovely. "Like a cook my wife once had who played the numbers she dreamed."

"Exactly!" Jane replied, feeling her narrow escape.

"Well, in any case," Mr. Ernst was still chuckling, "you *are* on my wave length. I've dreamed about this one too, all right. I know the president personally, have investigated the company firsthand. I look for a stunning performance. Say a hundred?"

Losing her voice, Jane found herself waggling two fingers like the hard-pressed school child of an earlier day. Only in this case the signal meant two hundred. Anything worth buying at all was worth buying well. Her own notebook said so, although of course Mr. Petry's actual words had been, "Be cautious about putting all your eggs in one basket. Diversify carefully."

In contrast, Mr. Ernst was obviously a more knowledgeable, more experienced being. He smiled his satisfaction, observed, "You do, of course, have a cash reserve."

"Oh, yes." Jane bounced right back, and by now her tone placed her cash reserve at close to half-a-million.

"Proper balance between stocks and bonds?" Mr. Ernst's soft voice make things sound more like an observation than an inquiry.

Her heart in her throat, she volunteered, "If anything, I am a little heavy on bonds."

"That may be a pity, you know." Mr. Ernst needed reassuring.

Not knowing a bond from a hole in the ground, Jane could tell she had flubbed and said the wrong thing. Thus she hastily borrowed a highly reassuring phrase she had heard Mrs. Hope use. "I am living," she said, "on my interest." Her voice strained and her throat tight, she plunged on. "I am not touching my principal."

"Oh, well," Mr. Ernst beamed his relief. "I had not understood. In that case, *certainly* two hundred."

Reaching for his telephone, he asked her, "The name of your broker? I'll place the order for you."

Reaching back in her memory, Jane suffered, muttered something about having no memory for names. But the very first customer's man she had met came back just in time to avoid disaster. He was the Bide-a-Wee Hotel enthusiast, the young man with the manicure. "Oh, yes," she clapped her hands. "Mr. Kilgore. Mr. Kilgore of Hocum and Pullem's. And please also order twenty shares for a young friend of mine." She gave Mr. Ernst Eleanor's name and address.

With dispatch, Mr. Ernst crisply gave Jane's double order to an astonished young man who would not have dreamed of questioning the wisdom of his dean. Her crisis over, all Jane could think of now was Al, and how thrilled *he* would be.

"First thing tomorrow morning," Mr. Ernst smiled at her.

Thus it was, before its respectability had impressed the pony stalls in the front offices, that Jane purchased Lone Star Electronics at 16—200 shares for herself and 20 for Eleanor's $300. Lone Star Electronics was a diamond field not yet discovered, a blue chip still pink in its infancy, a missile not yet even fueled.

At the showdown, she had succumbed to the mental imagery of Texas—that and the excitement of electronics for tomorrow's world. Besides, among its other activities, this surging, booming, infant company made seismological instruments. What more appropriate stock, she asked herself, could an earthquake baby possibly buy?

To heighten her expectancy, Mr. Ernst had even said, "Won't you let me serve you at any time? Professional courtesy, of course." Meaning, no fee, she supposed, to a colleague's widow. And he had added, "Besides, I'd love to see you," and he had said this in such a sweet way that Jane, looking at a face that seemed oddly familiar, felt a stab of loneliness, and for a split second she dreamed a silly dream.

Still, she defended herself. The others had said only, "Drop by anytime."

There was a difference.

# TWELVE

O ne Thursday evening about a month later, when Wally had skipped class to be with Eleanor, Jane and Mrs. Hope went to Otto's and sat side by side on the high stools. Mrs. Hope was bubbling over. She had just found the "ideal" investment counsellor, a Mr. Van Heusen. In an awed voice, she told Jane, "He refuses to take telephone calls or to be interrupted when you're with him. He's so masterful." Mrs. Hope was too full of Mr. Van Heusen to remember to drink her coffee.

"The first thing he did," she went on, pounding the counter, "was to give me unshirted hell. I swear it, he took one look at my record book and fainted dead away. He was simply divine. He even called me a trader." She added knowingly, "In sophisticated circles, 'trader' is really quite a dirty word. Mr. Van Heusen wouldn't even *speak* to Mr. Evans." In her emphasis, Mrs. Hope almost fell off her stool.

Jane's heart went out to Mr. Van Heusen, in part because Mrs. Hope was Mrs. Hope, in part because she was feeling the least bit sorry for herself anyway, and therefore sad for everybody else.

It was now Spring, and class was ending with only two more sessions. Things ought to be beginning in the Spring, she thought, not ending. But, at least, thanks to a teacher's hard case of mumps, Jane had been teaching for three weeks—which was the only right thing about the Spring thus far.

Bringing her sorrow closer to home, she now told Mrs. Hope, "I'll miss class. I have dearly loved it." She would miss her teammate too. Mrs. Hope was perpetually awash with good cheer.

95

"Yes," Mrs. Hope sighed and sipped her cooling coffee. "It's been fun." She added grimly, "Besides, it helps keep me busy. I'm so bored with travelling. I've done everything but ride a camel. Thank God, I'm still avoiding that." Jane knew her friend was only seeking, not bragging.

"We'd better get busy checking each other's list," Jane reminded her teammate. Their final and best lists of stocks were due the very next time class met. Then the teacher would have time to compare and judge them and, at the *last* class session, announce the winner.

"Wouldn't it be hysterical if *I* won?" Mrs. Hope's face lighted like a sparkler on the Fourth of July. "It would be almost worth cheating to see what he'd do."

Aglow with delighted surprise, Jane suddenly realized she and Mrs. Hope were both already cheating like fury. Of course, she couldn't tell Mrs. Hope about the Countess—that was off the record. And now when she tried to tell her she was still sticking with only one stock for her final list—Lone Star Electronics—Mrs. Hope wouldn't believe her. In fact, she hooted.

"Oh!" she laughed merrily. "You've always said that! But don't bother. I don't really care, you know, if you haven't remembered to tell me about your others."

Mrs. Hope handed over her notebook for inspection. As for her gyrations in the market, the teammates quietly decided that the time was too short to prepare a full listing, or even a current one with all its percentage gains or losses. Besides, Jane thought to herself, it would turn Mr. Petry prematurely grey.

"He might even be hurt." Mrs. Hope looked stricken. "The poor man might think he hadn't taught me anything."

Thus a sticky problem was settled between friends. Mrs. Hope said she would go over her records before class met again and just pick any old six stocks in order to hand in something. And this was a relief; Jane could easily see how complicated life could get on the students' side of a teacher's desk.

At that moment Miss Gertrude Green, the corporate lawyer, came up with her coffee and stood at their elbows. Jane liked Miss Green. All the girls considered her really too charming to wrestle with such an unequal weight as the law, which they saw as an impenetrable solid. Right away Miss Green agreed that it was too bad class was ending.

"Maybe," she smiled, "there's a graduate investment class we could join!"

Turning to Jane, Mrs. Hope said, "You're so studious and all, always thinking about things. Why don't you form a class and teach it? I'd adore it!"

Despite the fact that her teammate was known for going overboard about an idea, Jane smiled happily.

Suddenly, however, she countered with an inspiration. "Why don't we," Jane leaned forward in her excitement, "form an investment club? You know, meet once a month and really invest?"

Both Miss Green and Mrs. Hope were electrified. The idea was too wonderful to let drop even for a moment. Before they'd returned to class, certain decisions had been taken. Since Miss Green was busy all day in her office, Mrs. Hope and Jane offered to divide up the telephoning and present the idea to their classmates.

Thus it was that the next day before evening, they had organized The Mudhens, sixteen in number. It was especially exciting to have Miss Green and also the lovelorn columnist, Mrs. Helen Spalding. Like the class, the club boasted women of distinction. To everybody's surprise, even Mrs. Henry Hayden-Critchfield III, of millinery fame, cooed, "How delightful! How really elegant." She pointed out, "Ten years ago a canasta club was the thing. Now it's investments!"

It was agreed all around that the first meeting would be at the home of Mrs. Stephens on Twin Peaks. Mrs. Stephens thought this beginning would be peculiarly appropriate to her ambitions. A tiny wren of a woman with a deep voice and aggressive black eyes, she was well-to-do, was mildly predatory, and clearly expected—by virtue of her money and natural qualifications—to be elected The Mudhens' first president. In fact, it was she who named the club, before anybody else really knew it was named.

But something untoward happened during the very last class meeting to sidetrack Mrs. Stephens' presidential ambitions, and she was to hold this eternally against Mr. Petry.

\*  \*  \*  \*  \*

In fine fettle for his last class, and determined to make one final large impression upon pupils he hoped to attach as clients, Mr. Petry quietly waited until Mrs. Hayden-Critchfield had passed inspection in a purple satin turban that swirled upward and would have given high tone to a circus pony.

Gravely, the teacher passed around mimeographed copies of the ten stock lists that had made the greatest gains since last October. In fact, a little sheepishly, he admitted he passed around the *only* lists that showed actual gains; all the rest—in a class of 40—showed losses, mostly minor except for one ghastly slump of 80 per cent.

"It is a happy thing," said the teacher, shuddering, "that such a dip is purely imaginary."

Naturally, he did not say who had pulled this extraordinary blooper, but Jane, with her practiced eye, thought she could tell. Confident that she herself was the star pupil, and feeling her oats, she wrote a pert note to Wally, "The psychologist flunked!" Wally snorted. True, Mr. Petry was at his kindest and softest best with the psychologist that evening—explaining, excusing, and finally blaming an eccentric market.

Then came the big moment. Reaching behind his desk, Mr. Petry brought forth an eye-catching silver and lavender package. It was garnished with sequins and the girls loved it. Stepping forward, he held up a sheet of paper upon which, with high visibility, he had scrawled a large red "A." Smiling benignly, he announced, "Mrs. Stephens' portfolio of eight stocks has nice diversification and shows a gain of 15 per cent. This is excellent indeed." Everybody clapped and, while Jane's heart did a flip-flop, Mrs. Stephens half rose from her chair to go claim the prize. But Mr. Petry, possibly out of a subconscious desire to award it to Mrs. Stephens as a glittering future customer, had really made a booboo. Recovering awkwardly, he quieted the girls and signalled that the climax was yet to come. "Mrs. Stephens placed second," he hastily explained, and Miss Gertrude Green is third with six stocks and a splendid gain of 13.9 per cent." Mr. Petry asked Miss Green to take a bow. Then he cleared his throat.

"There is among us," he said, sounding like a minister of the gospel addressing a convention of rock-and-rollers, "that *rara avis* in financial circles—a successful speculator. It so happens, as it would not happen again in a hundred years, that the most un-usual and irregular paper handed in is also the only one whose gain was greater than Mrs. Stephens'." Making a steeple with his fingers, Mr. Petry confessed he had wrestled over the decision. Then he tried to strike a lighter note. "Let us be good sports," he said, although nobody except Mrs. Stephens had yet thought of being a poor one.

"I have decided," he announced, "to leave the final decision up to the vote of the class. *I* want to be fair. Sharp and Blarney wants to be fair. But should this pupil be permitted to win first prize? That is the question."

The class looked quietly torn.

"True," he went on. "During a sluggish, adverse market, this investor did better than 35 per cent. A remarkable achievement."

The class gasped and, in its suspense, began looking around to guess the winner. Mr. Petry held up his hand for attention.

"*But,*" he intoned, "this pupil violated every principle of sound investment I have tried to teach." Solemnly, he began ticking off the major sins. "Her so-called list contains a single stock."

At this, Mrs. Hope popped straight up in her seat as if a bee had stung her. She looked at Jane, nudged her so hard Jane winced. Then, quite audibly, she shouted, *"Merde!* I thought you were kidding."

Blushing, Jane shushed her.

Loftily ignoring the interruption, Mr. Petry repeated, as if to persuade himself, "A single stock." Then he rushed on. "There was no effort to achieve diversification. No attention was paid to corporate size, history or distinction. Finally, dividends were either ignored or forgotten. In brief, I am afraid this pupil was merely lucky in finding a four-leaf clover. Very lucky."

Wally, bored with all the moralizing and pretty sure he could guess the winner, suddenly began whooping it up. "Speech!" he called. "Speech from the winn-ah!"

Joining his mood, the girls began to applaud. Encouraged, Wally took to his feet and addressed Mr. Petry. "Professor," he said, "I move that we elect this genius of finance winner by acclamation." A fresh burst of applause broke over Mr. Petry's head.

Obviously taken aback, he bowed indecisively—as if the girls might be applauding him. Seconds later, finally conscious of having overcooked his moral, Mr. Petry thoroughly straightened his tie, stepped from behind his lectern, and strode toward the winner.

He beckoned to Jane to rise. While all the girls craned for a look and some squealed and others clapped; while the psychologist scowled; while Mrs. Hope screamed, "Bravo! Aunt Jane!" and while Wally whistled as at a basketball game, Mr. Petry gracefully presented Jane to the class.

Of course, she was not surprised; she had awaited this moment for months with Olympian serenity. Being a woman, she'd done the natural things: she had indulged in a new hair-do which was delightfully bouffant, and polished up her old silver beads and earrings until they shone like something right out of Tiffany's. Still, in the flush of accepting a paper grudgingly marked "A+," she turned totally, exasperatingly shy. She blushed, she stammered, she even put up a show of amazement in receiving the sparkling package. All told, she was the perfect picture of a fluttery valedictorian.

The prize itself seemed predestined. It was a handsome leather notebook for her stock record—firmly alphabetized.

Celebrating later with Wally over her beloved Irish Coffee at Tommy's Joynt, Jane borrowed his pen to make the first entries in her new stock book. Wally had not known of her purchase of Lone Star Electronics.

Then a terrible thought struck her and she hastily began figuring something on a paper napkin.

"Oh, dear, oh, dear." She began wringing her hands. "Oh, Wally, I won the prize dishonestly. What can I do? What shall I do?"

"How come?" Wally couldn't tell whether to laugh or commiserate.

"Don't ever, ever tell Mr. Petry," she begged. "The awful truth is that I actually bought Lone Star Electronics *before* the purchase date I put on my paper for him. I just *imagined* that purchase date for him."

"So what?"

"Well, look." Jane was almost in tears as she held up the figures on the paper napkin. "My gain is actually 50 per cent, not 35, as he thought."

"Oh, my God," Wally hooted. "Women!" He added, "You didn't lie *over* the amount you'd gained. You lied *under*. Don't you see? You shoulda won two prizes!"

Jane was quickly comforted, especially when Wally talked on.

"It should ease your grief somewhat," he said, "to think of what the Countess is going to do. Besides, you already have your 50 per cent gain in Lone Star. Not bad. Not bad."

"Mr. Ernst likes it too," Jane offered.

"Wally's eyes widened. "You know *him? August* Ernst?"

"Oh, yes, yes," Jane tossed off casually. "He bought it for me.

He's the nicest man I ever met." Then she paused and added. "He has such a *noble* face."

She wondered why she had been so fulsome about Mr. Ernst. She had seen him only once.

Wally did not order a second round. Obviously restive, he finally grinned and said, "Let's go. Eleanor is expecting me."

Driving to her apartment, Wally told Jane, "I never thought this would happen to me. I was a rolling stone, you know. But that little girl of yours—well, the whole truth is, I'm crazy about her."

Jane had never heard Wally talk like this. He sounded so sober, even so sad. Deeply puzzled, she didn't even try to reply. But she did reach to pat him on the arm.

# THIRTEEN

~~~~~~~~~~~~~~~~~~~~~~~~~~~~~~~~~~~~~~~~~~~~~~~~~~

Within a week The Mudhens met in Mrs. Stephens' home at 7:30 in the evening, and quickly made Jane's superiority official. Miss Green made the nomination and by acclamation, before Mrs. Stephens could get her own campaign off the ground, the girls swept Jane into office as their first president.

Mrs. Hope rushed to embrace her. "My teammate! Aunt Jane!"

Any among the group who really knew their president would have anticipated the first order of business, even before the other officers were elected. Standing proud and erect in front of the mantel, with sixteen chairs in a three-row semi-circle before her, Jane smiled her tremulous appreciation and heard her voice breaking with emotion as she went after first things first. Pointing out with irrefutable logic that "mudhens" was merely a generic term, she called for discussion looking toward selection of a name that would be "more pleasing to the eye and ear." The members all looked startled but nobody gave any trouble, not even Mrs. Stephens. She was still enjoying her sulk.

In rapid succession came the suggestions—Wall Street Witches, Montgomery Street Sirens, Gamblin' Gussies. Everybody quickly fell into the mood of cute alliteration and Jane joined in while the girls laughingly worked off their self-consciousness.

Finally Mrs. Hayden-Critchfield proposed "Girls of the Golden West." She had once sung the lead in the opera of a similar title, she offered modestly. Besides, everybody recognized the name as a double entendre—which showed group dynamics at its turgid best. In fact, Jane had just put this winner to a vote when Mrs. Hope cried out, "Amendment! Amendment!" Positively inspired, Mrs. Hope came up with "The Golden Girls of the West," which everybody adored except Mrs. Hayden-Critchfield, who was somewhat hurt—and this made for a delicate situation. In the end, however, she smiled her assent and the name was a shoo-in. It carried unanimously, with only the psychologist not voting. She held out for her own suggestion, "Neurotic Nellies," and the fact that her moniker had nothing to do with investing seemed to escape her. Anyhow, "The Golden Girls of the West" titillated everybody else.

The Golden Girls elected Miss Green vice-president, Mrs. Spalding recording secretary, and Mrs. Hayden-Critchfield treasurer. Then when everybody suddenly realized that Mrs. Hope, one of the club's founders, had not been rewarded with an office, Miss Green saved the day by proposing that the group have a sergeant-at-arms. Mrs. Hope won this by acclamation. Neatly and quickly the girls had boosted Mrs. Hope on top of the world, and her surprise was so radiant they went ahead and gave her a duty: the sergeant-at-arms was empowered to collect a $1 fine from anybody who failed to show at a meeting.

"Don't give me any trouble, girls," Mrs. Hope delightedly waggled a finger at them. "I'd hate to call in the sheriff."

Knuckling down to serious business under Jane's leadership, the group decided basic questions in short order. Three members would present three stocks for discussion at each meeting. All stocks were to be bought through Mr. Petry. Members would invest $25 each month—or a total of $400—and all decisions about what, when and whether to buy were to be settled by vote of the simple majority. Of the entire group, probably Jane was the only one who blanched at the amount of the monthly investment. But she didn't have the time now to feel anxious about that. Mrs. Stephens was asking for the floor. With a darkly conspiratorial air of expecting the worst, Mrs. Stephens rose in all her tiny height to say that every investment club should have an attorney to protect its interest and settle disputes. The club thought this idea was the greatest, and Miss Green graciously consented to serve, without fee, as legal advisor. "It won't take any time," she smiled.

Jane glowed. Things were off to a wonderful start. During refreshments—coffee or Sanka and cake—she realized she could scarcely wait for next month's meeting. The Golden Girls were going places.

*　*　*　*　*

One thing after another that summer made life seem good, and for the first time since Horace's death Jane began to feel like a whole-souled individual again—not only eager but also able to cultivate her own destiny and her own future. Heretofore, she realized, she had acted out of necessity and a feeling of being driven, but now there was a difference. As president of the Golden Girls, Jane felt a strong sense of direction, of having somewhere important to go. And as the proud owner of two beautiful stocks, she knew she was bound to get there.

Actually, life offered a tidy dollop of confidence to everybody that summer who owned any Lone Star Electronics. The shares Jane had purchased at $16 had shot up to $45; and her original investment of $3200 was now worth $9000, at least on paper. Eleanor now had $900 where she had begun with $320—and Al, with his ten shares purchased at 12, was feeling like a capitalist with his profits of $330. It was all he could do to keep from telling Rosemarie, but he had sworn to wait until her birthday, in December. "By then," he told Jane, "it may well be $500. Rosie will really swoon." Yes, life was being kind.

Then to cap the climax, one day in late July, Mr. Ernst called, in high spirits. "Now you *did* tell me you were fully invested," he said. "But it occurs to me you might care to look into the boom for leisure-time stocks—particularly bowling."

Knowing nothing of recreation stocks, Jane merely made welcoming noises, and Mr. Ernst went on to explain. "This country may be second in literacy and second in conquering space," he said wryly, "but by golly we're the undisputed masters in recreation."

Moreover, he had personally completed a five-day study of a young company that had doubled its size every thirteen months since 1954. "In short," he summed up, "it is growing at the rate of 90 per cent compounded a year. You just may want to consider a token investment. No more."

Even sophisticated Mr. Ernst, maddeningly calm as he seemed, was thrilled with his investigation. Jane could tell. As for her reaction, it far overshot his idea of a token investment.

"How much is it a share now?" she tried to keep her voice even.

"Last sale was 25, a new high. Up from 24½ yesterday."

Calculating boldly, Jane ordered 100 shares, an amount that would consume almost every sou of her remaining assets. The thought was intimidating, but not insurmountable. Not with Mr. Ernst on the other end of the line. He already owned the rich knowledge she had sought so desperately.

"I am not acquainted with your portfolio," he now reminded her. "Do you continue to hold your senior securities? In sufficient balance to permit a $2500 investment in a relatively unseasoned company?"

"Oh, yes. Yes, indeed." Jane sounded gaily offhand about her last $2500.

"Fine!" said Mr. Ernst. "Then it's 100 shares at 25. I'll order through your Mr. Kilgore." He added pleasantly, "Won't you stop in soon? I'd love to see you."

The sound of his warm, friendly voice sent her sense of well-being skyward. Yes, of course, the call had been purely professional. Yet he had said, once again, that he'd love to see her. But whether or not there was a tinge of personal interest mixed with the professional, the fact remained that a man of distinguished capabilities was generously concerning himself with her welfare. Jane was so profoundly moved by this that she told Al and Rosemarie, "Mr. Ernst is being so kind I keep thinking it's all a dream."

Actually, Jane was too exhilarated for several days to realize that Mr. Ernst's call had led her to violate her first basic rule for investing. The name of her new stock was perfectly horrid— "Amalgamated Pinspotters." Moreover, she didn't know what a pinspotter was, and the only image that came to mind was that of a baby playing on a rug. This didn't seem quite right. Nevertheless, it was fairly easy for her to reconcile to her self-betrayal. The third day after she bought it, her *Chronicle* showed Amalgamated Pinspotters closing at 27. Jane gently folded the paper back to its delivered state so that she could have the pleasure of opening it again to the stock market quotations.

Then she rushed down the hall to tell her friends. "I've already made $200!"

Rosemarie yelped, "What am I waiting for? I want to have fun too!"

Al said, "No! My God, no! One of us is enough."

Jane was so annoyed that Al was acting like a banker again that she went for her slide rule and her figures on Pinspotters. "Look," she tried to show him. "Just look at the percentage increases."

"I don't care," said Al. "This place is getting to be a damned racetrack."

"Woman's place," explained Rosemarie redundantly, "is in the home. Women have no brains."

"Right!" said Al.

"*You're* the only one who can have any fun," Rosemarie pouted.

"Damn right!" snapped Al.

Rosemarie said no more, but she thought plenty, especially after she dreamed that she and Al were buying a long, sleek convertible. She told Jane about it. "Snarkiest job you ever saw." Rosie had lots of confidence in dreams; once she had found a lost earring by dreaming where to look. Accordingly, two mornings later, on her way to work, she slipped into Jane's apartment and peppered her with questions.

"Is it too late to buy Pinspotters? How much would ten shares be? Will you get it for me? Will you promise not to tell Al until *after* it's doubled?"

Jane said, "If you hurry, you can probably get it for around two hundred seventy-five dollars, plus commission."

Her eyes getting bigger by the second, Rosemarie did some quick mental arithmetic. "I can buy ten shares! I've always wanted to own ten shares of a stock!"

Jane's confidence in Mr. Ernst, not to mention the world of bowling, overcame any qualms about her friend's impulsiveness. She promised to order it for her.

"Imagine!" Rosemarie hugged her. "Me in the stock market!" She ran out the door and off to Gump's.

Consequently, when Jane called Mr. Kilgore he greeted her warmly, took her order for Mrs. Rosemarie Bonelli, and then chided her gently.

"You know when you came to see me, you didn't mention that Mr. Ernst was your counsellor."

"Oh, didn't I?" Jane burbled her apologies.

"When he ordered Pinspotters for you," Mr. Kilgore went on in a burst of confidence, "I decided to pick up a little for my mother."

Jane had not exactly foreseen the day when she would help to season young brokers. But, generous-hearted, she gave Mr. Ernst half the credit.

By mid-August Amalgamated Pinspotters had made a neat eight point gain, and Rosemarie was so overcome she told Jane, "This calls for a celebration." Jane, too, had been aching to make some drastic departure from her normal routine. In the past, on occasion, when she was lonely and trying to make out from day to day without cashing in any stock, she had permitted herself a flight of fancy by pretending to be well off. Not that she would have known how to be either greedy or pretentious, and not that she and Horace would have given a hoot about keeping up with the Joneses. Imaginative as she was, money for its own sake had little appeal, and she never really visualized walking on a carpet of greenbacks. Her fantasies were simple dreams of money to pay her rent, buy new books, refurbish her tired apartment, travel a little, and treat Kim to more liver and herself to tickets to the symphony. Occasionally, too, it would lift one's spirits to call a friend and say, "Meet me at El Prado for lunch." This was the sort of fillip Jane had never known without anxiety. Consequently, her dreams really subtracted more than they added; they simply left out the anxiety. Nor should this be surprising. After all, an individual accustomed to sales of straw hats in January, winter coats in May, and turkeys in September does not come easily to new habits. The zest one has built up for coping goes dead, and its satisfactions are missed—even if they are those of a wiggling tooth.

But now she had to do something different, and it had to have flair. Just for a little while she had to have some fun. Something deep inside—something adventuresome and lovely and reassuring —was happening to Jane.

Going over to Al's and Rosemarie's the next Saturday noon she asked them offhandedly, "Won't you be my guests tonight at dinner? Say at the Fior d'Italia?"

For years Al had ached to go to the Fior d'Italia, San Francisco's oldest Italian restaurant and one of its swankiest. Loving his native foods, Al had talked about going there the way Mahalia Jackson sings about going to Heaven.

But he valiantly told Jane, "You're crazy. You can't afford it. The answer is 'No, thanks'."

"You are rude and vulgar," said Jane. "Be ready at seven. Can we go in your limousine?"

At 7:15, with great swish, Al turned over his old Volkswagen to the doorman as if it were a Bentley. Then the *maitre'd* escorted the three from the spacious foyer, past red-jacketed waiters, past a pepperberry tree growing right in the middle of everything, and finally seated them in a handsome black leather booth.

Enjoying their martinis, and enraptured by the accordionist, everybody decided to order something different in order to compare notes. A little later Jane, charmed by her Polenta with Chicken, was exchanging shares of it in return for Al's Tagliarini al Pesto and Rosemarie's Monaca Bianca. His Italian blood rushing to his head, Al carefully explained what every dish was, even to the obvious things. It was a festive, wonderful evening, and what with drinks and tips Jane spent $30. It was a daring thing to do. That is, considering that she had exactly $9.15 cash left. And no checking account; she had closed it out for Amalgamated Pinspotters.

Too "stock poor" to eat beyond the next few days, she permitted herself to think of a small nestegg she had vowed never to touch this side of dire emergency. Ten years before his death Horace had squirreled away in a joint savings account the sum of $250, which an aunt had sent him in a burst of generosity, and he and Jane had neither added to it nor subtracted from it since that time. But at least it still existed, and it had long served as her last line of defense. Her very last. In her new confidence, however, the sum gently rebuked her for her former timidity.

Quickly closing it out, she was scarcely overwhelmed by its accumulated interest of ten years. It represented, she figured, one-tenth of the profit Al had made in the stock market from a comparable sum in less than ten months.

The following day, at a furniture sale, she even splurged on a handsome nest of teak tables and a Shoji desk of rosewood. Now she would no longer have to do her stock market research on an old card table. The desk and tables looked ill-at-ease among her outmoded furnishings, but they symbolized a renewal, a beginning and a hope—as promising as tender buds in March. One had to begin renewing someplace.

Then, because a club president had to look nice, she purchased materials and patterns for three new dresses—a navy blue Italian silk, a sheer wool of olive green and a gold print with little grey lines in it. She didn't know until she got the latter home under the light that the little lines were actually letters spelling out "Kiss me." Maybe, she thought to herself with a start, I've reached the age where I *must* wear glasses. But, amused, she couldn't resist giving the print to Eleanor. Beaming, and pretending she had bought it for Eleanor in the first place, Jane told her, "It looks so like you. Young and gay!" Jane hurried and made it up for her in two days' time.

"I'll be terrified if anybody notices!" Eleanor said. The gold heightened the glint of red in her blond hair and she looked charming.

"Don't think Wally won't!" Jane gave her a sunny smile.

\*   \*   \*   \*   \*

Yes, for the wise ones, dollars could multiply like rabbits and the thought never really entered Jane's head these days that the market had been known to turn upon its faithful and bite like a bear. Still, in her serenity, there was one thing amiss. As her club's president, she felt an irresistible yearning to share with her sisters the munificence of Canadian Countess. This was something one had to be an insider to know. Yet she was pledged to secrecy by Wally. But did he still hold her to her pledge? Mr. Petry was surely not a threat these days. Finally, telephoning Wally, she told him of the new club and invited him to come address the group and let the girls know about the Countess.

Wally reacted like a thunderhead swooping low to an August prairie. He barked, "Good God, when did they start a club?"

He snapped, "Dammit, I told you this deal was in the family." Jane had never seen a man so upset over nothing, really, and she was immediately contrite.

So, apparently was Wally. He began telephoning every few days. "Most beautiful girl in the world up 3 cents today," he would say, vibrant with enthusiasm. "Up another 2 cents next week." One on his way to see Eleanor he stopped by Jane's apartment and confided, "The real secret of our success is merger. We've got four companies just standing in line begging to get taken in." He had written that once in her notebook too, she remembered.

As a matter of fact, however, Canadian Countess was not quite on schedule. When Jane bought at 25 cents a share, Wally had said the Countess would be $1 by summer, but with summer in full bloom, she had reached only 50 cents. Of course, there was a sound explanation and, Jane believed, a wise one. "We have slowed the price down to build carefully," Wally explained. "Things were too hot, going up too fast. We want a solid company, not a flash in the pan." Not that she ever got the exact picture. But, as Wally kept assuring her, she did have six thousand dollars now where she had put in only three. Too, mergers were merging all over the place. Under the circumstances, she would have felt ungrateful to ask questions. It was enough to understand the broader, deeper aspects of successful investing.

But if Jane was at all concerned about being thrust into the role of *grande dame,* she was a bit premature. All hell was soon to break loose in an unexpected quarter—at the very next meeting of the Golden Girls.

# FOURTEEN

~~~~~~~~~~~~~~~~~~~~~~~~~~~~~~~~~~~~~~~~~~~~~~~~~~~~~

The meeting was to be in a showplace inhabited by one of the sisters—a Mrs. Blaise d'Argent—in beautiful St. Francis Wood, just a stone's throw from the Pacific Ocean. The weather was warm and the evening soft and clear, and all the girls arrived in high spirits. Since Mrs. d'Argent's home was an authentic reproduction of a French villa, with gardens only slightly less formal than those of the Palace of Versailles, Jane finally had to call time on the sight-seeing. Thereupon the hostess—a handsome matron with a shy smile—ushered everybody through an inner courtyard and into an airless parlor whose museum furniture was never intended for human beings trying to think deep thoughts. With the scent of mildew in the air, the formal line-up of some sixteen high-seated, high-backed, high-armed oak chairs looked like nothing so much as a warden's nightmare. While the girls submissively filed into their quasi-electric chairs, Jane walked past a knight's armor, took her place up front by the side of a massive round table, wondered nervously whether it had belonged to King Arthur, and called the meeting to order.

Mrs. Hayden-Critchfield collected everybody's check for $25, Mrs. Spalding read the minutes of the last meeting, and the reports got underway. For all of half an hour, Attorney-at-law Gertrude Green was not to know what a mess she had let herself in for. Nor were the girls to appreciate how omniscient Mrs. Stephens had been in insisting they have her counsel. Mean-

113

time, it was enough to get used to their forbidding meeting place.

The three reports scheduled for that evening were to be given by Helen Spalding, Mrs. Hope, and Mrs. Stephens. Since the latter always had the spotlight by hook or crook anyway, and was bursting to deliver, the school teacher in Jane bade her call on the other two first.

Known as a quiet and effective member of Mr. Petry's class, Helen Spalding, without any to-do, introduced Union Automation as a "promising growth situation" at today's market price of $77. The more alert mutual funds had discovered its astute management, she noted, and she made a good case for a possible future stock split. As she went into some detail the members somberly took notes. Then came the question period, before the vote.

Mrs. Hope spoke up. "Is it a blue chippie?"

Mrs. Spalding, smiling tolerantly, couldn't rightly say. But potentially, yes.

Mrs. Hayden-Critchfield ran to use the telephone to ask her husband whether he knew Union Automation and how she should vote.

Jane spoke up. She had been reading big books again—this time to give proper leadership. "Do you know," she asked, "whether the board of directors and the president own any shares in their own company? I think practical management a wonderful idea."

Mrs. Spalding was prepared. All told, management owned 60,000 shares of the 600,000 shares outstanding.

Jane nodded contentedly. Obviously, enlightened management.

"How much," asked Mrs. Stephens, "does the company give to research and development?"

At this moment Mrs. Hayden-Critchfield, sniggering, returned to the group. Her call had got her husband out of bed. His only advice had been: "Get the girls to wear hats. And remember, San Francisco's women are the best dressed in the world!"

"He'd love me," interpolated Mrs. Hope. "Ever since my last hair tint I've worn a hat. Even at home. I tried 'Riotous Mauve,' and don't anybody else. Look!" From under her cloche she pulled out a sad lock of dull brindle hair the color of a rained-on boardwalk. "What's more," she wailed, wrinkling her nose, "it stinks!"

It took a little managing to get the meeting back to order after the sergeant-at-arms' disturbance, but the president finally gave the meeting back to Helen Spalding.

The girls voted to buy two shares of Union Automation at the next day's market price—with Helen Spalding looking as pleased as if she owned the company.

Foiling Mrs. Stephens again, Jane next called on Mrs. Hope. To her surprise, Mrs. Hope did not urge taking a flyer on real estate on the moon. Instead, of all things, she began to report on the Benjamin Franklin Mutual Fund. In fact, sounding like a contestant in an oratorical contest, Mrs. Hope was both ringing and well organized.

"For the past decade," she began, "only ten per cent of our 300 mutuals have done as well as or better than the Dow-Jones industrial averages. The reasons are two: first—indifferent or inadequate professional management, and second—management fees that are excessive. But among the top performers, the Benjamin Franklin Mutual is a brilliant star. It gives investors their money's worth. For seven years now the fund has leapt ahead each year by anywhere from 15 to 30 per cent. Furthermore, it is one of the very few funds that charges nothing beyond a small management fee, which is quite fair. Today's price of the stock was $11.19."

It was hard to believe it, but Jane was certain that her plump and pretty friend was talking, for once, without spoofing.

"It is very trying," Mrs. Hope concluded, "to pick a superior mutual. It is almost as hard as selecting an individual stock on the Big Board. But I can recommend, without qualification, the Benjamin Franklin Mutual." Mrs. Hope bowed and took her seat and the girls gave her a big hand. They also promptly voted to buy ten shares of Franklin Mutual. In the flush of her triumph, Mrs. Hope scribbled a note and passed it to Jane. The note said: "Bravo for Mr. Van Heusen! He wrote my report and I thought it spiffy, didn't you?"

Jane smiled. She should have known all along. Her friend was incorrigible. But she was nevertheless taking the Golden Girls seriously and this was a good sign.

There was no doubt in her mind. Before long the Golden Girls would be known through the Bay Area for their shrewd investments. How proud Mr. Ernst would be!

Now, no longer to be contained, Mrs. Stephens jumped to her feet and took over. With an ambivalence that smiled as it stabbed with an icicle, Mrs. Stephens confessed her continuing disappointment that her list for Mr. Petry had been outpaced. "I had been too conventional, too defensive," she addressed Jane directly. Even the mice in the knight's armor got the idea—Mrs. Stephens meant to make amends. Turning to the group, she began slowly to loosen her blockbuster. Not that she *knew*.

"Today I present a stock that is unusually aggressive," she smiled, "but it is so brilliantly managed and its prospects are so thrilling, that I know it will intrigue us all. In brief," Mrs. Stephens said, pausing for full effect, "this is like being offered American Telephone at 3¢ a share in 1912." Then she dropped her bomb. "The name of the stock is Canadian Countess. Some of you may remember Wallace Googins . . ."

Murmurs from the group began to ebb and flow in waves of astonishment. Smiling her surprise, Mrs. Stephens paused. Then two—or maybe it was three—voices spoke up in unison. "I already have Canadian Countess," the voices said. And they didn't sound like pleased voices. Quickly the murmurs swelled into an angered crescendo. Whatever it is human beings say when they are outraged, the mutterings of the Golden Girls burst as from a bunch of lady firecrackers set off by one match.

Then the peppering, the enraged voices of individual members. "A.T. and T., my eye!" somebody shouted.

"'The secret of our success,'" mocked one voice, "'is merger. We've got ten companies just bustin' to get in.'"

"Wally Googins has a very sick ego!" cried the psychologist. "Diffuse hostility."

For once Mrs. Stephens was rendered mute; she turned white, then red. And from somewhere, as feebly as from a distant cave, Jane forsook parliamentary procedure and protested an idiotic protest, "That stock is in the family and confidential!"

Clearly Canadian Countess was as confidential as a wheat field to grasshoppers. Mrs. Hope, banging her purse against one of the warden's chairbacks for attention, shrieked, "I bought 20,000 shares six months ago. I keep trying to sell it and nobody will buy it!" Her voice trailed off to a whisper, "*Merde!* I haven't even told Mr. Van Heusen."

Mrs. Spalding spoke up in a brisk monotone, "Two months ago I gave my 5000 shares to my broker. He told me then it was worthless and it still is." She suddenly took to her feet and asked quietly, "How many of us are in the Canadian Countess family?" Receiving no reply from her stupified sisters, since by this time the girls were hanging on the ropes, she asked again, and now she was sharp. "Raise your hands, those of us who were taken by Wally Googins!"

While Mrs. Stephens flailed her arms and screamed "No! No!," everyone present slowly, sheepishly, eventually raised her hand —with only one exception. That was Miss Green, who was looking upon the girls' undoing with a detached professional eye. Before this hour she had never heard of the Countess. Wally had never approached her. Now, sensing the group's need of a cheery note, she brightly offered, "We'll have to see what can be done." It was about as far as she could go.

Mrs. Stephens snorted, "Oh, you know everything will be all right. It just *has* to be!"

But hardly anybody could be comforted, especially, perhaps, the hostess, Mrs. d'Argent. Over lemon snow and cookies, which nobody could eat, she burst into audible sobs. Her party had been a bust.

# FIFTEEN

~~~~~~~~~~~~~~~~~~~~~~~~~~~~~~~~~~~~~~~~~~~~~~~~~~~

For the next few days Jane was a bit under the weather, and it could be that her *malaise* was psychosomatic. In any case, she stayed close to her apartment; she avoided Al, Rosemarie and Eleanor; she brushed Kim so many times he must have thought it was Christmas; she wrote letters to relatives she had not thought of in months, including the brother-in-law banker in Omaha who was Rosemarie's father. Above all, she missed Horace. He would have known what to do —even if only to go back to a savings account.

The plain fact was that for once in her career, Jane was involved in a set of nasty facts that didn't yield to her normal method of editing out the disagreeable. She found it practically impossible to take a bright view of anything. Actually, her only contribution to positive thinking during the first two days following the debacle was the conclusion that whoever named an "alarm clock" an "alarm clock" was a genius who should be celebrated, for it was sometimes as "alarming" as all get-out to be awakened to yet another day.

Gradually, certain facts began to fall in place, one of the first being the total of Wally's take. With the exception of Gertrude Green, The Golden Girls had invested anywhere from $500 to $4000 apiece in Canadian Countess—except for Mrs. Hope, who had sunk $5000. The grand total lay just south of $35,000. The sum was so vast, the situation so incomprehensible, Wally's role so baffling, that while the question of Jane's own $3000 invest-

119

ment lay tragically in her consciousness, not her least concern was for the Golden Girls and their future. Jane had not realized, until their future was in jeopardy, how much the Golden Girls meant to her—in purpose and in friendship.

Gertrude Green, who was looking into things, had promised to get in touch as soon as she had any information. Meantime, over and over in Jane's memories spun the fantastic montage of the girls' first reactions under shock. Mrs. Hope had wailed, "My God, don't anybody tell my ex-husband. He always said I was a boob with money." And there was the sweet-faced, little white-haired member, a Mrs. MacKinnon, who said nothing at all but just sat quietly weeping. Her legs were too short to reach the floor from that monstrous chair and she looked ill-equipped to cope with anything much. Jane was grateful when Miss Green had reached over to pat her hand.

But one thing she heard again and again, sounding like a parrot enchanted with the sound of its own voice, was Mrs. Setphens' wailing boast, "He took me to the smartest little French restaurants for dinner." This revelation had struck a particularly sensitive note. Why, Jane wondered, had Wally taken Mrs. Stephens to expensive restaurants? All he had done for her was to buy her *one* Irish Coffee. The rest of the time they had gone Dutch. And Eleanor? He had never taken her to expensive restaurants, either. That was the last, the very last, straw.

Knowing nothing about the ponderous machinery of the law, Jane became fairly dotty with the jitters during Miss Green's long silence. She practically lived by the telephone, which rang often as the girls began to call their President for advice—or more accurately, simply to report reactions, some of which were beyond Jane's powers of prediction.

Now the social scientists, for all their derring-do, have never done much in the way of predicting how fairly average unheroic people react to disaster, and a few oddball experiments here and there have only demonstrated what any man on a galloping horse would observe anyway—that people go right on behaving as they always have, only moreso. It's a time when one's latent talents and inner impulses may truly flower.

Thus Mrs. Spalding, on the one hand, treated Wally's betrayal as a vast social symptom. And her regular column suffered. Replying to the lovelorn, Mrs. Spalding strayed from giving simple, helpful advice and dug up little homilies about good character, about social responsibility, about the ringing eternal truths. Tediously, she even demonstrated how today's crop of loose livers portend the decline of the West. She became so serious-minded, in fact, that her editor called her in for a little private talk. "More sex," he ordered succinctly, "and less social reconstruction."

Mrs. Henry Hayden-Critchfield III, on the other hand, found wonderful stimulation in the debacle. Her first concern was to keep up a good front, and she telephoned to advise Jane how to do it.

"The Golden Girls must keep anything embarrassing out of the papers," she said. "Therefore, we must become known as *serious* investors."

So, just to counteract any scoop that might come, Mrs. Hayden-Critchfield proposed a capital idea: The Golden Girls of the West, in a body, should visit the Castlerock Corporation in Daly City because the Castlerock Corporation maintained a wonderful attitude toward visiting shareholders. A company photographer was always on hand, she had learned, to take the pictures of shareholders as they came into the plant and to present them with their fully developed pictures as they left.

"You see," Mrs. Hayden-Critchfield explained, "we'll have a marvelous picture of us all ready for the papers' financial pages. Or maybe society pages. We'll be right on the spot inspecting machinery and things. And looking terribly smart."

Jane started to ask whether her friend meant *clothes* smart or *brains* smart, but a more urgent question pressed itself. How

could the Golden Girls rate a picture with machinery or anything else? They had never bought any Castlerock stock.

But Mrs. Hayden-Critchfield was a thoughtful individual. Besides, she was the treasurer. "Just to keep absolutely legal," she
explained, "I am buying one share from Mr. Petry in the club's
name. It costs $7. We would not really want to take advantage
of any corporation." Mrs. Hayden-Critchfield sounded quite set
up. She could already see herself in the papers, looking stunning
in a breath-taking off-the-face creation. She was standing in the
front now next to Jane while the Castlerock president stood to
Jane's other side and charmingly lobbied for the club's approval
of his operations. Machinery was in the background.

Of all the girls' varied reactions to Wally's perfidy, Mrs. Hope's
was the most primitive and childlike. She swore she was going
back to Dallas. Nobody believed her, of course. Herself least
of all. Then the simply fell off her constant diet with more
than customary recklessness. She told Jane she had gained five
pounds in two weeks, and she added, "I can't imagine *how!*"
Revealing another phase of her reaction, she told Jane in confidence, "I don't honestly think the color of my hair is pretty
this time either, do you. Don't you think it's too, too copper?"

Hair tints were not on Jane's list of things-to-find-out-about,
possibly because she had never had the money tints require. But
as an editor, she welcomed any change for the better, whether
on nature's works or the human condition, and Mrs. Hope clearly
needed a lift.

"Tranquilizers just aren't enough any more," she said.

"Maybe more bronze than copper next time," Jane ventured.
"It would be lighter, more gay."

With the girls to watch over, to buck up, and to keep in line,
the fruition of Jane's own impulses were somewhat delayed. But
she was no person to feel trapped like a fly in a spider's web,
and as president of the Golden Girls, she felt a keen responsibility about doing something to help Miss Green. At the same

time, she wanted to plan a stunning surprise for the girls—not to mention Wally. And for Eleanor, who would eventually have to know about Wally.

Just as some people are born to be against everybody, Jane was born to be *for* everybody; and just as some people have a steely determination to prove everybody wrong, Jane seemed hell-bent on proving everybody right. Wally was a friend, and one did not cheat one's friends. Everything finally became as clearcut as that. Consequently, while she had dutifully telephoned all the girls and passed along their lawyer's warning not to call or see Wally during the investigation, Jane became hopeful that she could, with proper information, prove the Countess to be exactly as Wally represented, even without asking Wally himself.

Remembering Mr. August Ernst's kindness, she translated her decision into a course of action. A man in his position would surely know all about the Countess; and as Jane headed for Mr. Ernst's office—this time having called for an appointment—her heart was thumping like a trip-hammer. At last she would know the exquisite satisfaction of setting a hideous error right. Indeed, by the time she reached Mr. Ernst's firm, she was savoring the fantasy of seeing the Golden Girls fete Wally as their hero. Then, and only then, would she tell Eleanor.

As Mr. Ernst smiled and shook her hand, she realized with surprise that he was not quite the elderly patriarch she had first made him out to be. His hair was almost white, yes, but his big brown eyes were downright devilish—and yes, Jane could not deny it, they were also appraising her rather comfortable bosom. With no advance warning whatever (for her romantic, moon-swept emotions were a bit on the rusty side) she was once again suffused with pleasurable confusion—and happily mindful that while not model trim, she had a womanly figure. At least Mr. Ernst looked approving. Actually, her heart now remembered, he had approved the first time, too.

As if to explain his high spirits that afternoon, he gestured toward his desk. There, in a litter of corrugated wrappings, Jane saw a gay, impressionistic watercolor of a carousel—and it was so fey, so lively, that it seemed almost to make its own music. Delighted, she said this.

Mr. Ernst beamed. "I saw it on the Riviera last month," he told her, "and was so taken with it I bought it on the spot. It just arrived."

"Oh, how nice it would be to travel!" Jane explained, then bit her lip in embarrassment. Naturally, as the wife of a well-to-do investment counsellor, she had covered the earth as liberally as Sherwin Williams' paint, and then some. That is, if Mr. Ernst had asked her. But for some reason—probably involving delicacy—he did not. Instead, he motioned her to a chair, smiled, "Your Lone Star Electronics is doing very nicely. So is Amalgamated Pinspotters."

"It would be fun," she smiled and told Mr. Ernst, "just to see what a pinspotter looks like."

At this particular moment, however, she had things far more compelling to think about than either her paper profits or people's use of their leisure time.

"Some time ago," she began, "a friend gave me the opportunity to buy into Canadian Countess."

Mr. Ernst suddenly looked as if he had a bone caught in his throat. "I assume," he eyed her cautiously, "that you checked into your friend's recommendation."

"Well, not exactly. The facts he gave me seemed to speak for themselves."

"Oh," said Mr. Ernst.

Now moving to polish Wally's armor, Jane tried to ignore the grim edge in Mr. Ernst's tone. Taking her class notebook out of her purse, she began reading, with feeling, and gestures, Wally's various notes about the Countess. She ended with, "We'll salt the place with African diamonds before we'll let any shareholders get hurt."

Her listener was sternly unimpressed. "Two questions," he said brusquely, "First, how much did you buy? Second, where did you get that information?"

Jane plunged on—this time like a child on a tricycle losing her pedals on a steep downgrade. She told Mr. Ernst all about her class, about the Golden Girls, Wally, Gertrude Green—everything. She added, "Right now there is some misunderstanding about the stock. It seems that you can't sell it."

There was a long silence. Jane finally added, not too brightly, "I guess you can't sell it because nobody wants to buy it."

Not given to frightening ladies, Mr. Ernst held out his hand and kindly asked, "May I see the notebook you are referring to?"

She was only too proud to hand it over, and for long minutes by the clock Mr. Ernst studied the specific information it contained about the location of the property, the numbers of men already at work, the Canadian tycoon behind it, the coming mergers, and so on. The misspellings gave him a clue and he asked carefully, "Is this by chance your friend's writing?" Jane nodded her assurance.

"Would you mind telling me his name?"

"It's Wally Googins."

Mr. Ernst's face was stony as a statue's. Yet when he spoke it was with surprising tenderness. "Canadian Countess," he began, "has caused considerable trouble for some months now. It's a company that started out all right but now exists largely in the minds of an unscrupulous ring of salesmen. Your friend, I'm sorry to say, has been one of the chief offenders. In any case, the stock is now utterly worthless."

Jane's eyes grew wider and wider in disbelief as Mr. Ernst talked, and a shiver coursed along her back.

"California's Blue Sky laws take care of such shady deals," he went on. "That is, if there's something specific in writing upon which to build a case. Young Wally Googins' notes to you may turn the trick."

If Jane no longer had any choice about surrendering her illusions about Wally, Mr. Ernst's genuine concern for her made the wrench less hurtful. Still, the irony of what she had done set all her nerves aquiver.

"To think," she gasped, "that I should be the one to furnish the evidence against poor Wally!"

Explaining that stock market racketeers, or "the boiler room boys," prey on the inexperienced and the gullible, Mr. Ernst emphasized, "They are careful to transact their business by word-of-mouth, and not to put anything in writing. Then the law has a hard time getting at them."

Thumping Jane's notebook, he went on to explain that Wally's firm, Van Dyke and Buchanan, dealt in solid stocks as well as malodorous ones, and this fact, he felt, was the Golden Girls' trump card.

"I feel," he said confidently, "that the firm will settle out of court. Otherwise, they would have to close their doors." Opining that Gertrude Green would be ecstatic to know that such notes existed, and make a lawsuit a mere formality, Mr. Ernst paused thoughtfully and turned to study Jane.

With her head high but her eyes lowered, and her hands to her cheeks as if in thoughtfulness, Jane was unexpectedly feeling much more than she was thinking—and a little guiltily she realized that what she was feeling had little to do with Wally but everything to do with herself. And Mr. Ernst.

A shrewd and practical observer of human nature, Mr. Ernst was not quite finished with his questions, though he was clearly finished with Canadian Countess for the time being. Smiling broadly, he said, "May I ask you something on an entirely different subject? It comes from personal interest rather than plain curiosity."

With something new in her heart, a lilt she had not felt in many years, Jane looked at him, dropped her hands, and smiled her assent.

Vasiliu

Then Mr. Ernst shifted gears and changed his mind. "It's really not a question at all," he spoke softly, "but a comment." After a long pause, he continued, and regret colored his words.

"Your husband—I do hope you'll not mind my liberties—I've learned that you loved him very much, and I've also learned that he was not an investment man." There was no reproach in his voice, only sorrow that she had found it necessary to have an excuse to come see him—any excuse at all.

Her gentle deception exposed, Jane looked at him and then away, her eyes moistening. All she could say was "Forgive me."

"Forgive you? You're wonderful!"

Suddenly wheeling his chair around, Mr. Ernst reached into the credenza, took out the bottle of port and the two glasses. And his eyes were now merry. Holding the bottle high, he beamed, "Let's rev up our spirits! We have all sorts of reasons to celebrate!"

# SIXTEEN

~~~~~~~~~~~~~~~~~~~~~~~~~~~~~~~~~~~~~~~~~~~~~~~~~~~~~~~

U pon leaving Mr. Ernst, Jane ducked into a
drugstore, telephoned Miss Green, said she
was bringing her "a surprise," and then headed up Sansome Street
to the attorney's office. She had considered saying she had "an
exciting surprise." But she didn't. She couldn't. Her emotional
circuits were already overloaded.

She wanted no more excitement, no more emotional stress—
nothing that would disturb her lovely, vibrating sense of joy
about Mr. Ernst.

Her preposterous deception about poor Horace had both
amused and intrigued him. He had grinned. "Imagination is one
of the most interesting things a pretty woman can have." He then
kept her talking about herself.

Jane had told him the whole truth about Horace. "By all the
usual standards," she had said, "Horace was a failure. Yet he
was a dear, successful human being who owned his own soul."

Mr. Ernst understood immediately. He might have known
Horace always. "A man ought to be judged by what he *is*, not by
what he *does*," he had said.

It had been so glorious to share Horace with Mr. Ernst that
she hadn't been able to stop a natural flowing of thoughts that
seemed entirely appropriate for him to share—especially since
his responsiveness, now gravely attentive, now amused, now sympathetic, had charmed her utterly. She'd told about her teaching,
her job hunting, and about trying to scale the Matterhorn of the

129

market—despite the brokers. Mr. Ernst had shaken his head at this. "Some of them provide the best argument I know," he admitted with sorrow, "for investors doing their own homework." When she had finished with her story of the prize, and Mr. Petry's scolding, Mr. Ernst had laughed so hard he got out of his chair and held his stomach.

"You cannot escape me now," he had said when she left. "I know too much about you!"

Now hurrying along to Miss Green's, Jane took hold of herself and firmed up two major decisions. First, she would bury her treasure of thoughts about Mr. Ernst until she had a moment of leisure. She would have much, much thinking to do. Big thinking!

Next, she would regard Wally from now on with a cold and clinical eye. Mr. Ernst would encourage that, she knew, and this ought to help. Fond as she was of the young man, he had betrayed her and had betrayed her friends.

Jane reflected that she had never known a real crook. Amateurs, of course; they were everywhere. But never a *bona fide* professional. Weren't crooks supposed to have a furtive eye, a nervous tic, a memory for the combination of safes? Jane decided she must have lost touch with modern criminality. Apparently the old second-story burglar with an honest yen for jewels had been succeeded by today's smoothie, who makes himself ingratiating, and who prefers to manipulate people and have them *give* him their money. Jane thought about this with a certain admiration for the great skill required.

In fine fettle by the time she reached her destination, she was shown into a carelessly elegant office that was littered with books and papers. Seated at a pale mahogany desk in front of hand-woven drapes shot with gold, Miss Green looked more honey-colored than ever, and twice as official—especially when she put on her amber spectacles. Jane sank into an oversoft davenport and explained her errand, although, in handing Miss Green her notebook, her stout-hearted resolution about Wally went berserk. Sentimentally her mind latched onto his love of poetry.

"Wally was a friend," she mourned. "I still can't believe it."

Miss Green snorted, "Don't be naive. Our charming friend may be the coolest con man to hit town since the Gold Rush." Having scuttled sentiment, she began to take a long, careful look at Wally's paens about the Countess—while Jane sat and watched her and began to think unwholesome thoughts about lawyers. They were trained, yes; but were they also educated in the finer feelings between friends?

How simple life would be, she thought, if everybody were endowed with a legal brain. Then you could just slot people into neat categories—crooked or straight, daffy or normal, greedy or generous, mean or good, cold or warm, and black or white. There would be nobody with awkward grey shades in between. Nobody with looney impulses or untamed spirits or a long-distance dream that turned into a nightmare. Not a trace of any such specimen as an appealing, fun-loving young man who was perhaps as crooked as a dog's hind leg.

Although Miss Green seemed far away, Jane could tell she was beginning to purr like a winning lawyer, and now she explained, "Jane, you were so clever to capture things in writing! Tell me, how did you ever think to do this?"

Jane fidgeted, but Miss Green was too fascinated with Wally's fulsome details to wait for an answer anyway. She leaned back with satisfaction, removed her glasses and pointed them toward Jane. "The District Attorney will be th-rilled with your foresight."

Not being able to cope with the undeserved tribute, Jane did the next best thing. She smiled modestly, decided it was more comforting for the District Attorney to think her bright than foolish.

"But what in the world," Jane asked, "does the District Attorney have to do with us," For all she knew, district attorneys were something invented for TV plays.

Miss Green explained that at one time she had hoped to keep any suit against Wally in the civil courts. "But," she explained, "he violated the Corporate Securities Act, which carries a criminal penalty." Therefore the matter was out of her hands, and was clearly a case for the criminal court. "And it has to be prosecuted by the District Attorney." Miss Green added that she was helpless to do anything beyond assisting him a little. "He won't need much more than your notebook," she said.

Jane was thunderstruck. A criminal case! Her mouth went dry and her hand trembled.

"But I thought—all the girls thought—can't we settle out of court?" Her quick question, after all, had Mr. Ernst behind it. How could *he* have been mistaken?

Miss Green did not hesitate. "Not a chance. I'm not sure at this point, but the D.A. may also have to prosecute on a second felony—'Grand theft.' You see, even if Wally's firm made restitution, the money was taken and the crime committed. He must be tried."

The possibility of all these black details had never entered Jane's mind. She had supposed the Golden Girls would merely sue for their money back, and that Wally's firm would handle things simply, formally and with dispatch—the way the insurance adjustors managed a few years ago when Horace bashed into somebody's fender. But, now without warning, she saw Wally in stripes with a ball and chain around his ankle. Her friend Wally!

Preoccupied with the genius of the law, Miss Green was oblivious to Jane's alarm. "This looks like a simple one-two-three play," the lawyer explained. "There is little doubt that Wally made a material misrepresentation to you in writing. There was such a company as Canadian Countess before it went broke, but never as he represented it. Second, influenced by his misrepresentation—for material gain, you understand—you purchased his stock. And third, in consequence, you were damaged. There you are. It's really a quite lovely case of 'Grand theft.'" Despite her admiration of the case, the lawyer did sound a shade regretful when she added, "It is punishable by imprisonment."

"San Quentin?" Jane suddenly felt herself stalling for time. A ray of hope had pierced through her bleak thoughts.

"San Quentin. He may spend several years making potato sacks."

"Years?" Janis voice sounded very weak.

"Well, we don't know what defense he'll have, of course." Miss Green reached across to her bookshelf and brought down three forbidding tomes—*West's Annotated Codes*. Running through their indexes, she consulted them all—two on corporations and one on the penal code. Then she said, "Probably not more than five to ten." Biting her lip, she added, almost with a show of sympathy, "This boy is in trouble."

Knowing exactly now what she had to do, Jane negotiated her store of resolution and announced with superb calm, "I am not going ahead with this. I will simply destroy my notebook."

Miss Green looked at her as if she had suddenly gone balmy. And actually, the gleam in Jane's eyes was firmly illegal, which augured no good for the People's case against Wally.

Recovering from her amazement, and recognizing an unexpected adversary, Miss Green finally asked, "Aren't you being just a bit neurotic?"

"But," blurted Jane, "I *like* Wally, and I introduced him to a darling girl who may be in love with him. Thank Heaven she's out of town until school starts!" After summer school Eleanor had gone to visit with her family at Lake Tahoe.

This news gave Miss Green a moment's pause. "Well, is she or isn't she in love with him?"

"I don't even know!" Jane had the grace to realize she was being difficult.

"H-m-m. Now that is something," the lawyer sympathized. "But you must look at it this way," she went on. "Would you let this little girl jump off Golden Gate Bridge—if you could help it?"

Jane sagged hopelessly, and a corner of her mind taunted her for being a sentimental idiot. Nevertheless, all that came from her throat was a strange burble of protest.

Now Miss Green softly moved in. "Besides, I'm afraid you have an obligation to the Golden Girls. Without your evidence, they haven't much of a case. Actually, I question whether the D.A. would feel it had a chance."

As president of the Golden Girls, Jane saw herself in a new light, and it was a cold, bleak light. Stubborn as she was, she knew she had no choice.

Miss Green spoke kindly. "I don't think you would or could let them down." There was a minute of turbulent silence. Jane didn't say Yes and she didn't say No. She was in a mauve study, thinking again, and her body was rigid.

The lawyer finally went on to guess that the District Attorney's office would file criminal action immediately, but that the case itself would probably not reach trial for two or three months. Since it was now early September, this would mean November or December.

Then, taking a lighter tone, in an effort to buck up her president, Miss Green emphasized that a day or two before the trial would be time enough to "rehearse" the girls in how to be good witnesses. "I'll coach them myself."

This new thought was for a moment distracting. It had never occurred to Jane that witnesses had to rehearse. Miss Green was sounding just like a high school athletic coach. And Jane, feeling better now that her thinking was done and her conclusion reached, was seized by an impertinent image—a sweaty Miss Green bounding around in white shorts, a whistle around her neck, refereeing the Golden Girls in a court of law that somehow resembled a basketball court. A mean-eyed District Attorney was umpire.

"Mrs. Hope will need a little extra going over," Miss Green went on. "We do want the sympathy of the court. For instance, let's tell her not to wear her star sapphire. Or her mink stole. And not to talk too much."

Coming out of her reverie, Jane agreed. "Maybe an extra tranquilizer before her testimony."

Miss Green thought that a splendid idea.

Ready to leave, Jane reached out to take her notebook. Miss Green, however, picked it up and hung onto it ever so casually. "We'd better hold it here in my safe," she said. "That's the best place for our only evidence."

"But my own notes!" Jane protested.

Shrewdly, and with a great show of humor, Miss Green merely replied, "Oh, but suppose something happened to our evidence now. Would you and I want to be accused of compounding the felony?"

*     *     *     *     *

Jane streaked for home and, before recovering her breath, began making telephone calls—exactly fourteen of them. One by one, right through her dinner hour and on to late evening, she talked with every one of the Golden Girls she could reach, except Miss Green. Actually, Jane would have called a special meeting if it hadn't been for Miss Green. But Jane couldn't think of any gracious way to leave her out and she certainly wouldn't want her there—not at this crucial point. The law, as their attorney saw it, was clearly little more than a practical institution for cut-and-dried situations, and Jane thought it a great pity and a shocking danger to citizens everywhere that the law utterly ignored rich nuances of meanings and human relationships.

As she talked with the girls it became quickly apparent that, like herself earlier in the day, none of them, either, had the foggiest notion about the law and its baleful workings, nor had any of them dreamed that Wally was headed for San Quentin. Like Jane, the girls knew the D.A. in the movies and television as the unrelenting, eagle-eyed foe of murderers, rapists, kidnappers and such big-time operators who made headlines, but whom one did not *know*. And that a living, ranting, vengeful D.A. would wedge a classmate of theirs into his unsavory agenda divided them, considering everything, between concern for themselves and concern for Wally.

Mrs. Hayden-Critchfield said without real hope, "Poor Wally! Isn't there such a thing as a tiny, inconspicuous criminal court somewhere? At least without the publicity?"

Mrs. Spalding said, in an ominous analogy, "I don't like this a-tall. You don't ask a surgeon to lance a boil. If you do, you get involved in a big deal, a major operation. The D.A. will make big fat headlines out of this." She knew newspapers.

She went on to tell Jane she had invited Mr. Petry to dinner and had told him *everything*, which made Jane frown until Mrs. Spalding described his reaction. "You wouldn't have known he was the same man. He was in a towering rage. He said Wally had made a monstrous fool of him, simply monstrous. He said Wally had ravished his class right before his very eyes. That is exactly what he said, 'Ravished.'"

Jane felt a reflexive rush of pride in Mr. Petry's unexpected forcefulness, but the best was yet to come.

"Phil Petry swore," Mrs. Spalding sounded deeply gratified, "he was going to punch Wally Googins in the nose." She explained that there was only one reason why Mr. Petry hadn't: he couldn't find Wally. Nobody knew where Wally was. His office had said so.

To Jane the best possible news about Wally was that he was out of town, especially since Eleanor, her vacation ended, was due back within a few days.

Over the telephone and speaking as individuals freed from even the slight inhibitions they felt when in full body assembled, the Golden Girls responded to their president's call with a rather wide variety of peripheral views.

Mrs. Stephens, who could never admit to being wrong about anything, and probably still considered Canadian Countess a good buy, was sure everything would blow over. She said, "We'll get our money back—with interest."

The psychologist said impatiently, "The courts are medieval bastions of horror. All I need is my thousand dollars back. All Wally needs is a little therapy, not punishment." Jane agreed that Wally had doubtless suffered an early trauma.

Little Mrs. MacKinnon, the wispy, sweet-faced woman that nobody knew very well, felt that earthlings tended to be too punitive toward one another. She said, "Only God can judge and pass sentence." Not knowing quite what to do with this reaction, Jane decided that Mr. Petry was at least practical.

As Jane made her calls, the only really excessive emotional reaction came from Sergeant-at-Arms Hope, who screamed, "My God, will they hang 'im? Or gas 'im?" It took a bit of effort to quiet her down.

The important fact was that nobody, really nobody, wanted Wally punished. Slapped gently, yes, but no prison pallor, no serious embarrassment to his carefree romp through life. Of course, Jane had known what the club members' reaction would be even before she took her soundings. For women of her age, and she no less, had all been indoctrinated in permissiveness. Because of her teaching, Jane may have known this better than most.

Moreover, the girls genuinely liked their sunny classmate. Until Jane had talked with them individually, however, she had not dreamed Wally had been so attentive on such a wholesale scale. But now their reminiscing came tumbling out. He had frequently played golf with Mrs. Hayden-Critchfield and poker with her husband. Any number of times he had taken Mrs. Spalding bowling, Mrs. Stephens to dinner and other classmates riding in his new car. And Mrs. MacKinnon had said, "I so enjoyed playing hymns for him to join me in song."

Wally's camaraderie with Mrs. Hope had taken still another tack, which goes to show how accommodating he was. At dinner one evening, just after he had his new car, Mrs. Hope recalled, the two had impulsively decided to drive to Carmel. "It was a sporty, divine week-end," Mrs. Hope had sighed in enraptured recollection.

Jane didn't quite know whether or not she understood the implications of such sophisticated talk. But in any case, Sergeant-at-Arms Hope didn't sound a bit like demanding an eye for an eye.

At the same time, even though the girls' sense of outrage had cooled by now, most of them were distressed about their losses. They wanted their money back, and the hard workers among them could not afford shenanigans any better than Jane.

Having sized up their attitudes, Jane saw her problem clearly; moreover, she saw her problem as carrying with it her duty, by virtue of her office, to solve it. After all, she was president, and high office carries high obligations. Breaking it down, she studied its three parts: (1) Get the girls' money back, (2) Save Wally from prison, (3) Save the Golden Girls from appearing up and down the length of the West Coast as the silliest bunch of geese ever bagged in or out of season. One aspect of the dilemma, she sensed, might be a little sticky: How, in a court of law, could the complainants defend the defendent? Jane wasn't exactly sure a rampaging district attorney would understand the girls' delicate point of view.

# SEVENTEEN

~~~~~~~~~~~~~~~~~~~~~~~~~~~~~~~~~~~~~~~~~~

Mr. Ernst telephoned to tell Jane he'd been thinking about her scaling the Matterhorn of the stock market. "I can just see you standing in a footsling—driving pitons in the Matterhorn's belly," he said. "Only trouble is— you look more delighted than grim." Laughing, Jane had to admit she'd had a lot of fun.

He also said he was sending her something he thought she'd like, and an hour later she was still at a high pitch when a taxi delivered a thin package wrapped in white tissue paper. Ripping it open with luscious expectancy, she finally uncovered his charming watercolor of the carousel. A note in his scrawly handwriting said, "I shall miss this. May I come see it soon?"

It was too much. While Kim romped around shredding the tissue paper, Jane sat right down and had an ecstatic cry. Some women do cry when something tells them they have reached a turning point in their lives. But Jane was weeping for more than that. What Mr. Ernst was really telling her was that he was lonely too.

She decided she didn't want to call in Al and Rosemarie to see the carousel—not quite yet. Rather, she needed just a moment of sharing this fey and brilliant painting with Mr. Ernst alone, for she knew he was thinking of her.

Then an inspiration hit—and she thought he must be omniscient. For she felt the quick desire to hang the new painting on the wall now occupied by her Chinese ancestors. She had long loved them, yes. They were exquisite of line, and years ago, in a burst of extravagance, she had paid a whole month's teaching salary for them. But they did belong to the past, which they seemed to guard as something holy; and come to think of it, they weren't really enspiriting at all. Just solid and venerable. In a ridiculous flash, the impression crossed her mind that the ancestors were not unlike certain blue chip stocks—deified for what they had been in their prime, but without vital juices now.

As she kicked off her pumps, stood on the old davenport, took down the ancestors, and pounded a proper nail in the wall for the carousel, it seemed suddenly to symbolize the young and spirited side of life—which beckoned with its eternal sense of quest, its brightness, its rhythm, and its love.

"Bless him," she said softly. "Bless him."

It was now full September, and Horace's savings had seeped clean away. Jane had used up all her defenses to protect her stocks, and now, ironically, she decided to give up even her substitute teaching. This would be a wrench, but there really wasn't much choice. She knew, without anybody's telling her, why calls for her service during the past school year and become fewer and fewer. It was simply that younger teachers even on the substitute list were selected first, and the older ones last. Consequently, the confidence she had once brought to teaching was now riddled by the knowledge that she was second or third choice. It was better, she told herself, to avoid the hurt of being a wallflower in the profession she esteemed so much.

She didn't let on to Al and Rosemarie. She made no comment at all until she had withdrawn her substitute's application. Then she told them, "I have retired!" Even up to a parody, she gaily recited, " 'No more school days, no more books. No more youngsters' dirty looks!' "

Al smiled. "You're a filthy rich dowager anyhow."

It was evening, and she and Al had sat down at the kitchen

table, over martinis, to talk things through while Rosemarie helped Eleanor unpack. She had just that day returned to San Francisco after spending the month of August with her family. The school year was opening, she was all preened for it, and she and Rosemarie would shortly join Al and Jane for dinner of chicken and waffles.

Meantime, Al loved his chance to talk with Jane about the market. As he well knew, she continued to study hardly any the less for having driven in her pitons securely. Without being the least uneasy about her two stellar performers, Jane firmly believed in keeping a weather eye on them. Nothing in years, in fact, had appalled her so much as hearing Mrs. Stephens say that she bought for keeps. "Once bought," she had said, "I file my stocks away and forget 'em."

Now Jane told Al darkly, "Mrs. Stephens regards her stocks as keepsakes. Some morning she'll wake up and find 'em out of style. The market creates new fashions faster than Hattie Carnegie."

Jane was never troubled by what she'd heard brokers call sloppy weather; she merely expected it, as one expects rain. For wasn't the historic direction of the market perpetually upward, save for the squalls? To be sure, it always had been. But the separate markets within the market were another thing.

Just as if she and Al were back in her old high school class, she now showed him some new charts she had made on shifting fashions, and tracing with his finger, Al saw how the food chains, drugs and utilities all moved steadily upward while, during exactly the same recent period, a host of other industries sank fast—among them, natural gas, rubber, cement, oil and steel. In another dramatic year, he could see how mining stocks had shot up one hundred percent while tobaccos fell twenty. Then, months later, things reversed, with the tobaccos going up while mining stocks went down.

As Al soaked up her lesson on the flow of investment capital from one industry to another, she quietly announced, "I may set a new house rule."

He looked up sharply.

"If I find my stock on the down end of the seesaw, I'll try to limit my losses to ten percent." Even the prospect of selling her baby blue chips brought tears to her heart. "In that case," she went on, "I'll switch to an industry that's on the rise."

"A lousy trader!" Al accused, grinning. He had picked up the cant.

"No!" She stoutly denied this. "I prefer 'strategist'."

Her bumptious word gave them both a laugh. But she did admit, to herself, to being deeply troubled about what kind of investor she really was. Mr. Ernst had said, "The thing to do, fair weather or foul, is to stick with brilliant management." What would she really do, she wondered—sometimes a little panicky—if her brilliant stars began to fade?

Al was saying, "My portfolio doesn't exactly suit me. It's not diversified enough. Hell, I've got only one stock. I've got to adopt a new strategy."

Jane poured him another martini while he lighted a fresh cigar. Al had taken to cigars almost exclusively now, had traded his old brown Volkswagon for a red one two years younger, and was spending his lunch hours in a broker's office watching the board—on the theory that a man with ten shares of Lone Star Electronics had to keep in touch.

Jane smiled. "You'd better leave your strategy up to Lone Star. But right now *my* strategy is to sell something in order to eat."

He pulled at his lower lip, finally said, "How's your Canadian Countess? How about selling some of that?"

"Oh, no," said Jane. "It's getting riper and riper." True, she told herself, in a manner of speaking.

"Then sell a few shares of Pinspotters." As he knew, Amalgamated Pinspotters had gone from 25 to 80, at which point—

weeks ago, now—it had split three for one—to give Jane 300 shares instead of 100. And Rosemarie thirty for her ten. Since then, the price had been stuck at 30.

"You're right" Jane nodded in agreement.

"You see," said Al didactically, "it's resting after so much activity." With the passion of the convert, he dearly loved explaining things to Jane. He leaned forward and lowered his voice. "I heard about a little honey down on Montgomery Street today. A boating stock. Not a word, now. Rosie's coming any minute."

To Jane's eternal surprise, Al and Rosemarie had still not told each other about their separate stock purchases. Having hit the jackpot himself, he had by now comfortably centered his old ambivalence about the stock market itself on the idea of women in the market; it was no fit place for a woman, particularly his wife, who was bound to get skewered. "It's a man's game," he said flatly, ranking it with bronco bustin'. Rosemarie had dismissed Al's attitude on the subject by explaining to Jane. "It's the Italian in 'im."

It was largely because Al expected women in the market to be euchered anyway that Jane had not yet shot off her rocket by telling him about the Countess. To tell the truth, she said to herself, weighing the finer points, she was a trifle uneasy about what he might do, for she well remembered his longing "to swab the decks with Wally" if anything went wrong.

But Al's mind this evening was on her welfare, her sale of stock, and on the painting of the carousel, which had come only the evening before. Having admired it once, he got up out of his chair in the kitchen and went into the living room to examine it, and for a long time he stood in front of it, just thinking.

"Really beautiful," he pronounced it. In truth, however, he was feeling unaccountably vexed about the picture, and not unlike a frightened child. What, he thought, if Jane left them?

But he nobly said, "I want to meet this gent some day. I really do. He must be quite a man." He turned, looked Jane full in the eyes, and added grimly, "And by God, he'd better be."

With perfect candor Jane replied, "You will like him. He will like you." Reflecting that Al, sweet as he was, seemed to be a little bossy about Mr. Ernst did not surprise Jane as much as it might have. Particularly now. In certain ways, Al had changed, and Jane couldn't help reflecting that money, even in small amounts, could bring out people's unsuspected talents and interests. Like a new father, Al was pretty possessive these days.

She always would think it was thought association that made him say now, "Why don't we go ahead with that dinner we were going to have for Eleanor and Wally or Petry?" Probably, Jane smiled to herself, Al would have liked to say, "I want to pass on Ernst." However, that might be, Al was now off.

"We'll have all Italian food," he said firmly, pouring himself another martini. The Fior d'Italia had aroused Al's nationalistic taste buds.

Rosemarie came in, shaking her head unhappily. "Eleanor's not herself," she whispered. "You'll see. She's coming in a minute."

"Maybe she needs a helluva party," said Al. Martinis always made him gregarious.

Jane was concerned. She, too, had noticed Eleanor's mood. "The child has no spirit," she said. "We had a little chat last night."

"Maybe she's not well," Al offered. "And if it's not female trouble, then it must be male trouble." He waited a reasonable length of time for applause, which was not forthcoming.

Rosemarie merely said, "Don't have another martini."

Al went on doggedly. "Anyhow, we've got to buck her up. A party would do it. With *cioppino*."

While Jane and Rosemarie prepared the dinner Eleanor came in and sat on a kitchen stool. She was wearing her toreador pants this evening, and while she looked 18 in face and figure, her eyes were those of a troubled woman.

"Aunt Jane," she asked, "could I please have a glass of milk? I'm starving. I forgot to get any food, really."

Jane poured her a full glass and patted her on the cheek.

Al said, "We were just going over plans for a big party. You can bring as many men as you want—Professor Petry, old Wally, your principal, anybody." He turned to Jane. "I think it would be nice to have Mr. Ernst. I'd like to feed that man."

"Who's Mr. Ernst?" Eleanor and Rosemarie asked the question at the same instant. Eleanor was eying Jane over the edge of her glass.

Al told Jane, "Let me tell 'em." He walked into the living room, took down the carousel, brought it into the kitchen and propped it up on top of the refrigerator.

"Mr. Ernst just gave this to Aunt Jane," he said brusquely. "Now that's enough for you two for now. She'll keep us posted."

"But that's heavenly!" exclaimed Rosemarie. "Of course Mr. Ernst must come."

Jane, furious with herself, was blushing beet red. Finally she said, "You're all terribly sweet. But not this time, really."

Al turned to Eleanor. "How many will it be? Let's not have any pipsqueak of a party."

She set her glass on the table and held her hands to her face. "I don't know. I guess nobody."

"Well—how about—about Petry?" Al was losing his exuberance fast; he sensed that he'd blundered into something, that this little girl he was fond of was hurt.

"No—no. Just nobody." Then she looked at him defiantly. "I'd have Wally if I knew where he was. You don't like him but I don't care." Bursting into tears, she slipped off the stool and ran out the door.

"Oh, Christ," Al said softly.

Rosemarie could only splutter.

"Don't blame Al, dear," said Jane. "It's all my fault, from the very beginning." Jane didn't go on to explain, perhaps because they already knew what she meant. At least, she told herself, surely, surely, such behavior on Eleanor's part does bespeak volumes. Little Eleanor was in love with Wally.

Rosemarie didn't want to ask the question, but she had to. "Where is Wally?"

Jane answered as lightly as she could. "Out of town, dear. Out of town on a business trip. But he'll be back."

They all fell silent.

In twenty minutes, outwardly revived, Eleanor reappeared, kissed Al affectionately on the forehead, and told him, "I hate you, you big lug. Go ahead with your party. I'll have Phil Petry."

Well, thought Jane, maybe Eleanor did mean it. Women in love were sometimes defiant. Especially young women.

They all decided to have the *cioppino* dinner the following Sunday night, and Al appointed a committee to help with preparations—reserving for himself the skilled part of the cookery. "We'll have only fresh fish from the sea," he said grandly.

Consequently, early Saturday morning, calling on Brawny Tony down at Fisherman's Wharf, Jane bought fresh halibut, prawns, clams, oysters, and tiny California shrimp, and then rushed home to help Rosemarie chop up the chard. Al made the tomato sauce, in a ten-quart marmite, which was enough *cioppino* for the U.S. fleet, and into the marmite, with the air of a highdomed chef at the Fleur de Lys, Al tenderly dribbled the chard, some red peppers and a *soupçon* of practically every herb on the place—thyme, oregano, basil, rosemary, marjoram.

"We'll taste it about six o'clock tonight," he promised them.

At six o'clock Jane ran over to help pass judgment. Al smelled, tasted ten times, gave everybody a taste, solemnly added more oregano and basil, tasted again—being very accomplished, very Italian.

"Now!" said Rosemarie. "The wine!"

"Oh, no, no." Al was appalled. "Tomorrow, about the time old Petry shows up, we put in one quart of red wine. Not an instant before."

"And then the fish," said Rosemarie.

"*Si, carina.*"

If only, Jane thought, we can get through the evening without mentioning stocks. And if only Phil Petry is sporting enough not to speak of the Countess. Surely he would be.

Promptly at six o'clock on Sunday evening, Al opened his door, whistled shrilly down the hall toward Eleanor's apartment, and everybody began converging upon Jane's apartment at once—Al with the hot marmite to put on her stove, Rosemarie with the bread and wine, and Eleanor with Phil Petry in tow. She looked determinedly gay, he looked happy, and his cowlick was standing on end.

The party started with an unexpected bang when Phil Petry, still shaking hands with Al, confessed, "My name was spelled P-e-t-r-i until my grandfather got mad at his father and changed the 'i' to 'y'."

Right away Phil had to accept a cigar, then a martini, then a footstool. He put his feet up, leaned back, forgot Eleanor, and no two old Yale men finding each other in Minsk ever wrought gayer rapport in a shorter time. It was a bore for the women.

Conversation at dinner was lively, and, after the Italo-American convention settled down, safely centered on Al's job. This, too, was fruitful; Phil's uncle was a banker in Sioux City. Thus the first bowl of *cioppino* went smoothly, and Al winked at Eleanor.

It was the second bowl of *cioppino* that brought trouble.

Al began the long slide to disaster by asking Phil, "Do you know Lone Star Electronics?"

"Sure," said Phil happily. "I bought some. Now 212½. Going

to split soon. Hope you have some." Phil didn't look at Jane as he said this, and this may be to his credit. He had never heard of it before it won her prize.

"Your star pupil told me about it, you know," announced Al.

"Oh! Then you got in early," said Phil, and at this point, to Jane's amazement, he turned to give her a dazzling smile.

Too bad, she thought, that Al cannot speak up. But she should have known better. For human nature at its worst was coming in for an inning. Al felt more like bragging than waiting for Rosemarie's birthday.

"I bought in at 12," he said, with a supreme effort at casualness. "Ten shares. Now worth two thousand one hundred and twenty-five cabbages."

"Oh, brother!" Phil whistled. "I bought late, at 60. But you had an advantage." Again, he smiled at Jane.

"I beat you," Eleanor teased him. "And I have twenty shares!"

By this time, with everybody talking at once, Rosemarie was staring at her husband. "*What* did you say, Al dear?" she asked with deadly sweetness.

Looking like a small boy caught in the cookie jar, Al grinned.

"I was going to tell you on your birthday. Pretty nice present, huh—to learn you're practically rich?"

Rosemarie looked furious.

"Peace!" soothed Jane.

Then Rosemarie threw caution to the winds. "You're not the only market buff. *I* bought Amalgamated Pinspotters before the split! I got thirty shares for my ten!"

Thinking she was kidding, Al snorted, "You did not get in the market!" Hadn't they—or at least he—always said one of them in the market was enough?

Al and Rosemarie were seated at opposite ends of the table, and Jane was looking from one to the other like a fan following a tennis match. Then the silence fell. It lasted a minute longer than forever.

Rosemarie finally broke it. "I was going to tell you as soon as it had quadrupled," she appealed to him, for she had, she knew, hurt Al. Her voice trembled. "It's just a few dollars short of that now."

No matter her or even their profits; profits were purely incidental. Al was looking at Rosemarie as if she had suddenly announced that all boy babies under six months were to be slaughtered. Then he, too, spoke, addressing Rosemarie like a patriarch seeking an excuse for mercy. "Tell me, did you also buy Canadian Countess?"

"Oh, God have mercy," moaned Phil.

"What's Canadian Countess?" It was Eleanor, her eyes bright with curiosity.

"I never got to buy the Countess!" shouted Rosemarie. "And it's all your fault!"

In the ensuing chaos, a remnant of Jane's mind paused to record gratitude to Wally. At least he had been kind enough to keep Eleanor out of it.

"What's wrong with it?" Eleanor turned to Phil.

An honorable rival, Phil Petry looked supplicatingly toward Jane. "Haven't you told her?" he asked.

Al stopped glaring, Rosemarie stopped biting her lip. Everybody turned toward Jane.

She tried to assume an air of what-will-it-all-matter-in-a-hundred years? And so Jane smiled with dignity, like a woman who wants to be remembered for her courage after the firing squad is done. It was the quick-triggered decision of an individual fortunate enough to get born in an earthquake. Her fingers even showed a little post-quake tremor. But she told herself, Eleanor is young. She can take it. She will have to take it. Miss Green was right. You don't let a friend jump off Golden Gate Bridge.

"The truth is," Jane heard her voice sound unduly thin,

"Canadian Countess was not exactly what it was represented to be. I am afraid Wally acted foolishly in selling it to me. I acted foolish in buying."

Al and Rosemarie looked stunned. Al finally said, "A slicker like I said, huh?"

Phil Petry could not resist adding, "He persuaded every woman in my class to act foolishly." Under his breath he added, "It was mass murder."

"GO ON!" Al's voice was that of Captain Bligh.

"Well," said Jane. "Let us not get overwrought. My other stocks are wonderful."

"What happened?" Again Captain Bligh.

Jane continued more firmly, "I feel that my $3000 loss is a sort of *tuition* expense—the cost of learning a great deal fast."

"Have you lost *all three thousand dollars?*" Al was on the verge of a stroke.

"Oh, no, no, we are suing," Jane quickly explained. "We will recover practically everything. It was misrepresentation for material gain, you see. That's illegal."

"Oh," said Al, icily, "Yes, I see. Misrepresentation is generally illegal. Yes, it is." He actually clinched his fists. "That skunk. That bastard, that . . ."

Eleanor didn't wait to hear anything more before she ran to put her arms around Jane. "Oh, I was so afraid of something wrong, and I didn't know what. I got so I couldn't bear hearing about 'special situations!' "

So Eleanor had sensed something was wrong, and whatever she was now feeling, she was taking all this like a soldier.

Yet Jane, still wincing inside from Al's words, had a sudden realization of her own "misrepresentation" to Mr. Ernst—and for her own "material gain!"

The thought alarmed her so much that she was only dimly aware that Al and Phil were flipping a coin—"The winner," she heard Al say, as from a distance, "to get the first punch at Wally." Then when he won he began to rage with frustration because Wally couldn't be found. "If only I can locate that son of a bitch. If only."

# EIGHTEEN

~~~~~~~~~~~~~~~~~~~~~~~~~~~~~~~~~~~~~~~~~

The next regular meeting of the Golden Girls was bound to produce trouble for somebody. The members were in a state of nerves and just a little testy—not with each other but with life's mischances, which did impose a strain. Mrs. Stephens was feeling put-upon even before she arrived. Picking Jane up in her car, she carried on a monologue all the way about how tiresome her broker was.

"I tried to buy Electric Eel at 35," she stormed. "He insisted I buy Van Dyke Razorblades instead. I did, at 80. It is now 62. But Electric Eel has gone up six. Oh, I'm furious."

Jane sympathized. The brokerage business did seem to be a pretty inexact profession. Every time she bothered to look up the Bide-a-Wee Hotel chain it had dropped another notch.

That everybody's spirits needed lifting became clear the minute the girls assembled on the dot, at 7:29. They were meeting in Mrs. Hope's very chic apartment on Russian Hill, but not even the magnificent view nor the fire in her marble fireplace rated any attention, for the girls were worried, rebellious, and obviously aching to *do* something about something. But, of course, what form their action would take had yet to be determined. As their president, Jane was all but intimidated by her responsibility.

Normally enough, she opened the meeting by calling upon Miss Green to tell the girls what *she* had already told them about Wally and the criminal court.

"We owe everything to our president," Miss Green began

153

sweetly, and with professional pride went on to explain how, as the club's attorney, she was signing a warrant for Wally's arrest. "Misrepresentation for material gain" was the terrifying phrase that wilted Jane as she thought again of her own deception of Mr. Ernst.

That harrowing report finished, the meeting steamed ahead as the Sergeant-at-Arms noisily interrupted proceedings by wheeling around a serving cart loaded with liqueur bottles. The president had never seen so many bottles outside a bar. Mrs. Hope could offer brandy, benedictine, uzo, creme de menthe, white or green, kimmel, cointreau, galliano, kalhua, or chartreuse.

Having served everybody except Mrs. MacKinnon, who declined alcohol, Mrs. Hope went right to the heart of her sisters' mood and into the spirit of things.

"Girls!" she cried with enthusiasm, "Let's give somebody hell right away. Just anybody."

"Maybe we *ought* to send Wally to San Quentin. But I for one just can't." It was Mrs. Hayden-Critchfield speaking. She was wearing a red velour fez-type creation that evening and, for a change, the girls could see her eyes, which were pleading. But they need not have been.

For, to the president's joy, if not exactly to her surprise, Mrs. Hayden-Critchfield had released the spring of tension. The group's *esprit de corps* shot as high as that of the U. S. Marines as they all began cheering for Wally. Mrs. Stephens grumped, "He's no worse than my broker any day." Mrs. Hope threw in, "*Merde!* He just got too enthusiastic. Who among us hasn't at times?"

The law was being scuttled even faster than Jane had hoped, and Miss Green was regarding her sisters with frank annoyance. Losing an argument already won, she spluttered ineffectually—but she looked too sincere to make any headway.

Mrs. Stephens began to orate. "And so, I say, let us recover our money. But let us tell the District Attorney we won't stand

Vasiliu

for any nonsense about sending Wally to prison." At this everybody applauded, which was unusual in such a small, informal meeting.

Miss Green snapped, "The District Attorney is not accustomed to being told what he can and cannot do."

"Now, Gertrude," Helen Spalding began pleading, "don't be like that. We all feel terribly guilty not to crack down, but you know we'd feel guiltier if Wally went to prison."

The moment was troublesome, the atmosphere heavy, but the logic in this was undisputable. And then Helen Spalding, whose social conscience was a daily problem, made a brilliant proposal that took everybody's conscience off the hook.

"If we are shirking our duty," she continued, "we can make up for it in the broader sense. Let's profit from our experience by working for better corporate management everywhere, better stockholder relations across the board."

This proposal was so thrilling and opened such vistas for do-gooding that a thoughtful hush descended upon the room. It was the psychologist who finally broke it with an unkind observation.

"Nobody, but nobody, is more conscious of a well-kept home than a dirty housekeeper," she intoned. She might have been reciting an aphorism.

It was a telling thrust and not anybody present could think of a retort. Nobody even tried, possibly because the psychologist had a point. Still, the girls dismissed it as minor.

Jane knew that Helen Spalding had lit the torch that might show the way out, and the president took over the meeting with a lightness of heart she had not felt in days. "We have heard our challenge," she said, her voice vibrant, and she smiled upon the girls like a teacher bestowing a prize. "Let us then go forward. Let us begin our march toward better corporate management for all stockholders!"

It was a mighty challenge, but nobody knew how mighty. Thus everyone was deeply gratified.

From this moment on, it was a sobering day—sobering for corporate management, that is. The girls' ideas about corporate reform began to flow, and the torrent grew so rapidly that the recording secretary couldn't keep up.

Right off, Mrs. Spalding herself offered, with the group's help, to draw up a Declaration of Conscience—a title she'd purloined from somewhere—which would serve as the Golden Girls' credo about "corporate morality," a heavy phrase that gave Mrs. Hope a pain in the neck. Mrs. Spalding added somewhat coyly, "I'll clear all suggestions with Phil Petry when I see him tomorrow night." This statement gave Jane quite a start. Apparently, Helen Spalding and Phil Petry were seeing a good deal of each other; at least, Jane remembered this was the second time Helen had mentioned seeing him lately. Perpetually bewildered these days about little Eleanor, Jane vowed to catch up with a thing or two.

To be worked into the Declaration of Conscience, the girls adopted, as fast as they could talk, certain weighty principles:

First, corporations were to be examined for their true spirit of democracy. The shareholders' voices should be heard. "It must never be forgotten that corporate officers are in the stockholders' employ." This was Miss Green speaking; feeling better, she was daring to be legal again, and her point made a terrific impression. Few of the girls had thought of it quite that way. Mrs. Hope asked, "You mean we can *fire* top officials?"

"The stockholder is king," Miss Green replied.

The possibilities pleased Mrs. Hope so much she beamed, "I'm going to start a list."

Next, stock ownership in their own company was an absolute "must" for a company's directors. Mrs. Stephens brought up this point, and in support of it she quoted a famed woman investor's tangy remark to support the psychology of such stock ownership: "People are much more careful with their own peanuts than they are with other people's emeralds."

"Touché!" somebody yelled. "Every director's got to have a real life interest in his company's profits!"

Next, the entire group felt that some limit should be put on executive salaries, bonuses and benefits, and on this point Jane's study and reading showed through. She chilled the group by citing, by name, a certain company whose six retired ex-presidents—a hardy crew who struck the girls as peculiarly long-lived—continued to receive annual pensions amounting to $1,090,674.31. "This sum seems a trifle exorbitant," she suggested, "inasmuch as this company's regular employees have no pension plan at all." Shocked, the girls clucked their agreement that this was exactly the sort of corporate abuse they must look into.

Their Declaration of Conscience roughed in, it occurred to several members simultaneously that their next immediate need was for a corporate culprit—somebody to take action *against*. Thus was Mrs. Hayden-Critchfield seized by the impulse to telephone her husband; maybe he could make suggestions. Immediately, the hostess plugged a telephone into the living room so all could help with the conversation. Mrs. Hayden-Critchfield got her husband out of a poker game.

"Look, dear," she explained hastily, "we're spoiling for action. What's going on around here that we could investigate first-hand? A company that stinks, you know. It overloads its executive salaries, romps over its stockholders, and all that."

"Something really scandalous," a voice urged.

"Strictly financial, not sexy," Mrs. Hope offered.

Mr. Hayden-Critchfield thought and thought, and finally left the telephone to consult with his poker partners. Then he rushed back with news that lit up his wife's face as orchids from Ziegfeld once had. A sort of expectant growl came from the girls as they awaited her news. Finally, she put the phone in its cradle. There was an electric hush.

"Well," she announced, "Just guess! This is absolutely marvelous. The Castlerock Corporation is raising its executives' salaries at the same time it's skipping its quarterly dividend!"

"No!" several gasped.

"Too divine to be true," somebody said.

"Henry says there's a stockholders' meeting next week! And it's only a few miles down the peninsula!"

Never had the Golden Girls had a finer moment, for now they had a Cause.

"Let us," said Helen Spaulding, "make protest fashionable!"

"It's a new day," opined Mrs. Stephens, "for the American stockholder."

"What a noive them Castlerock people do have," grinned Mrs. Hope. "They'll be sorr—ee!"

Jane remembered Mrs. Hayden-Critchfield's mention of the Castlerock Corporation, and in fact—thinking nothing of it at the time—she had received notice of its forthcoming meeting. This was the company that took visitors' pictures, and she also recalled that her friend had hoped the club would visit it in an entirely different connection.

As if reading Jane's mind, the treasurer reminded, "We own one share of Castlerock."

"What's its dividend?" somebody asked.

"Ten cents."

The girls giggled.

"Well, they're skipping it, and it's the principle of the thing," emphasized Mrs. Stephens.

"We would have one vote. The stock is in the club's name," said Mrs. Hayden-Critchfield.

"I move that we attend the stockholders' meeting in a body," proposed the president, redundantly. She forgot in her excitement that as president she should let others do the proposing. "All this will help us determine what good corporate practices are. We'll be in a better position to help management." Always, even irritatingly, Jane held to her conviction of the power of positive thinking.

Nevertheless, her attitude gave Mrs. Hayden-Critchfield an idea, and it lighted up the whole room.

"How about establishing an award of merit—a Golden Girls of the West Award of Merit?" she exclaimed. "Then we can award it to companies that really measure up. It will mean something, be sought after."

The idea, quickly seconded into a motion, carried unanimously, and Jane, enjoying her vision of corporate presidents seeking the Golden Girls' endorsement, promptly appointed a committee to design a fitting plaque. But all this was for the future. "Now back to Castlerock," said the president, and she warned, "Let us keep an open mind. Maybe Castlerock had a good reason for omitting the dividend."

For once Jane overreached herself, and her plea for fairness was dashed by a motion from the psychologist. It was so dramatic, so sensationally apt, that the girls, who ordinarily detested her, could have hugged her.

"I move that we go to the meeting in mourning," she said. "Everyone of us in widow's weeds, grieving for the lost dividend."

"This is marvelous!" cried Mrs. Hayden-Critchfield, who immediately pictured herself in a black veil as delicate as a butterfly's wing.

Carried along on the swell of enthusiasm, Jane could not resist the rueful reflection that, as a widow, she had come a long way. She who had refused to wear widow's weeds because people might think her helpless but would now happily wear them in her militant cause. And she couldn't wait to tell Mr. Ernst!

# NINETEEN

~~~~~~~~~~~~~~~~~~~~~~~~~~~~~~~~~~~~~~~~~~~~~~~~~~~~~~~

Looking vigorous and handsome, Mr. Ernst came to see his carousel, to take Jane to dinner, and to talk over his forthcoming speech before San Francisco's Society of Security Analysts, a group he had several times served as president.

He confessed, "I've spoken before the boys so many times I'm all tuckered out on subjects."

They dawdled pleasantly over his own special cocktails. Bringing along a bottle of Pernod, he showed Jane how to make martinis taste "less aggressive" by touching them up with the merest *soupçon* of Pernod, a trick he had picked up from a bartender in Monte Carlo.

Then for dinner he took her to one of his favorite hideaways—a beautiful little self-styled French restaurant called La Petite Chaise, which amused him because its chef was Chinese, as were all the waiters. "It makes for eternal surprises," he explained. "You order steak Chateaubriand and likely as not they bring you Won Ton and Egg Foo Yung. It could happen only in San Francisco!"

That evening, having ordered Chateaubriand, they were served lobster in black bean soup, sweet and sour spare ribs, and snow peas with water chestnuts, and Mr. Ernst grinned like a triumphant seer.

Enjoying mellow candlelight with their improbable dinner—with a French chanteuse singing softly in the background—Jane

161

was emboldened to suggest a subject for her friend's speech before the analysts.

"Maybe," she ventured, "the Society could do something about better standards for brokers."

Mr. Ernst was delighted. "I'll propose that! I'll do it, so help me. The president of the New York Stock Exchange has hit on that very subject. Some 15,000 brokers in this country ought to be selling potatoes, not stocks. Yes, yes, a wonderful idea."

Pleased to be taken seriously, Jane brought Mr. Ernst up to date on the Golden Girls. Roaring at their plans for the Castlerock stockholders' meeting, he told her an exciting detail about the company.

A huge and proliferating corporation, it usually had its annual meeting at its main plant in New York. But *this* year, he said—and his eyes sparkled at the surprise awaiting them—the officers were "hiding out" and meeting in their California plant for the very purpose of avoiding stockholders, most of whom were concentrated in the East.

"Go to it!" he said. "Those boys have no damn business upping their salaries when they can't make their dividend."

After dinner the two walked to a secluded little art shop on Post—the expensive kind that Jane had only window-shopped—and Mr. Ernst insisted on selecting an exquisite Chinese vase for her collection of jade pieces.

Later, at home alone with Kim, she found him enormously curious about the new vase. He walked around it for minutes, examining and sniffing and then curling up beside it—right on the ebony steptable. It struck Jane with a sense of wonderment how nice it was that Kim, too, had taken to Mr. Ernst.

At the core of the Castlerock Corporation lay an old-line mattress company; hence the company's name, which made you think of "a mattress fit for a king." Around this core, an aggressive new president, whose reach was longer than his grasp, had wrapped a new empire from mergers. To a specimen of his mass market mentality, the very word "merger" symbolized magic, and it didn't really matter too much what was merged, or in what condition—just so, at intervals, *something* new was added. For to his mind the very process of merging spelled growth, fiscal alertness, sharp operating—the sort of thing that might land him, steely-eyed, on the cover of *TIME*. Consequently, by the time this tycoon made ready for his California meeting, his company consisted of a series of uneasy affiliates: a one-piece chemical toilet company designed for rural customers and for the airlines; a fiberglass boat outfit which, because boats could be equipped with chemical toilets, was considered a stroke of marketing genius; electronic garage doors, which meant they opened automatically; a small paper mill, which smelled up a little town in Calgary; and, for the food industry, electronic bean sorters, egg weighers, and peach fuzzers; and finally, cameras imported from Japan.

Because of his wide diversification, actually, the president— his name was Pim M. W. Feegle—had been heard to say, many times, that buying into his company was just like buying into a mutual. The only trouble was, Mr. Feegle had failed to realize that electronic peach fuzzers and garage doors, not to mention toilets and fiberglass boats, were not likely to make any greater profits under the blanket of merger than they had been making singly—unless their managements changed, which they did not. Mr. Feegle kept everybody on, intact—which gave him the opportunity to create any number of new vice-presidencies.

Thus a conglomerate of individual products, all assailed by furious competition, were sapping profits from the core of the corporation, the mattress company.

Last year, facing facts boldly, Mr. Feegle and his Board of Directors decided to throw millions of dollars into research in an effort to bolster both business and stockholders, who are always passionate about research. Mr. Feegle pointed out, "The three hot words today are growth, merger and research. We are weak on the latter."

But nobody considered that only so much research can be done on a product like a one-piece chemical toilet. An engineer consultant was put to studying the optimum height and he advised raising the seat three-eighths of an inch, for Americans *are* getting taller; a designer came up with new color schemes, and created a model with a sidearm for magazines, and also a footrail; but a plumber couldn't do much about the fundamentals.

The research attack on the garage doors ended nowhere, for once a thing is automatic it's automatic and cannot always be made more automatic. As for the Japanese camera makers, they were not interested in Mr. Feegle's kind of research; their own ideas were a generation ahead of his anyway. In sum, the money spent on research improved the financial position of those to whom it was paid—but not Castlerock's.

Nevertheless, as the head of a mushrooming company—and it *was* growing sideways at least—Mr. Feegle, his eight vice-presidents and other top officers, including his public relations director and *his* eight assistant public relations directors, strongly felt the need of more attractive executive compensation. After all, their responsibility, along with their domain, had greatly broadened, and Mr. Feegle could be persuasively eloquent about this because it was true. Thus it was that his Board of Directors, after a lunch of four old-fashioneds and two chicken breasts *marengo,* enthusiastically gave all top executives a handsome across-the-board raise, plus bonuses, plus stock options, plus—finally—increased emoluments in retirement. As Mr. Feegle told his vice-presidents, "This is all quite a package, quite a package. A signal victory for good management."

Indeed, prior to his meeting in California, Mr. Feegle had not encountered any opposition of any kind.

The stockholders' meeting was to begin at 10.30 A.M. in a hole-in-the-wall theater, rented for the occasion, and for just one hour, in Daly City. Surburban to San Francisco, and to the south, Daly City lies in a perpetual pocket of fog, especially dense in the mornings—which suited Mr. Feegle fine. The drizzly locale would doubtless discourage the attendance of ubiquitous stock-holders.

Yet at 10:20 A.M. sixteen middle-aged women, some greying, some lean and some stout, and all dressed in widow's weeds with long black veils, could be seen picking their way down a side street in Daly City on their way to the movie theater. Jane and the Golden Girls looked like wraiths stumbling through the moors of an English movie. In three members' cars they had all driven down from San Francisco after meeting at the Mark Hopkins for early breakfast.

There, with their mood failing to match their dress, they had caused some little consternation. They had eaten too heartily, laughed too much, and drunk too giddily of coffee to command quite the deference such garments usually rate. Besides, none of the waiters could remember what recent mass disaster had caused such mass widowhood.

The president had read the girls the notice of the meeting, which stated the following purposes: "1. To elect directors for the ensuing year, and 2. To transact such other business as may properly come before the meeting or any adjournment thereof." Admittedly, the agenda didn't look loaded.

Now, as the girls filed along in Daly City hunting the theater, Mrs. Hope suddenly yelled, "Look!" and there, five feet in advance, it loomed out of the fog. Its double feature of B pictures displayed, to one side of the lobby, a gorilla swinging along to his forest home with a leggy maiden screaming in his arms. And on the other side of the lobby a second poster portrayed grim, heavily armed American paratroopers descending from the

Heavens toward God knew what rescue. Maybe, Jane hoped, the paratroopers from the one movie could somehow capture the gorilla from the other.

Inside the theater, which was still dark, the girls all groped their way to the powder room, snapped on the light, straightened their veils, and heard their president's final pep talk. It was brief and formal. "We shall acquit ourselves well for all shareholders, whoever and wherever they may be." It was now 10:28 and the sergeant-at-arms, checking the layout, reported that the house lights had come on full tilt and the corporation's officers were assembling on the stage.

This was precisely the moment Mrs. Hayden-Critchfield was waiting for. "Timing is everything," she instructed the girls. Accordingly, as she held the door, she reminded everybody walking past her, "Be dramatic! Move slowly. You are grieving, grieving!" She sounded like a hypnotist. Then, with their president in the lead, and Mrs. Hayden-Critchfield right behind her, the girls began to walk in single file—solemnly making their way down the center aisle and through a silent audience of perhaps seventy-five people. In view of all the hurdles management had erected, Jane was amazed and gratified to see that so many stockholders had leapt over them. She was also pleased to see six men on the stage, though obviously some top officers and Board Members were playing hookey.

The girls made quite a spectacular appearance. For an instant, stopping to look around, Mrs. Hope got the giggles and briefly threatened proceedings; but on the whole the widows' march generated precisely the high pitch of curiosity they had hoped for.

Especially from management. Mr. Feegle, a big man with lantern jaws and thinning hair, was sitting on the stage in a high-backed chair in the middle of his line of officers. He had trouble believing his eyes. As the widows kept on coming and coming, he even cupped his eyes once with his hands, like an Indian Scout, to make sure he was seeing what he saw. Then, barking to his

Vasiliu

lieutenants, to the left and to the right, he demanded an explanation. It was a futile demand.

Finally, on the two short front rows in the middle of the theater, the mourners quietly took their seats.

To Jane's complete consternation she realized that Mrs. Hayden-Critchfield, sitting next to her, had begun actually to weep. On her cheeks, under her gossamer veil, Jane saw the tears shining like diamonds. "Heavens to Betsy," Jane said to herself. Then she remembered. A professional actress, her friend was bred to be convinced of mood and illusion and bred to respond. But of course! Mrs. Hayden-Critchfield, so to speak, had hypnotized herself.

For an instant, Jane was at a loss. Then, the teacher in her coming to the fore, she commanded, "Hold those tears! It isn't time yet. We may need 'em later."

Old pro that she was, Mrs. Hayden-Critchfield straightened up, wiped her eyes, and smiled brilliantly.

Mr. Feegle was so harried by the black garments massed immediately in front of him that his voice cracked as he opened proceedings. He said awkwardly, "We are gathered here to, ah, to, ah, ah—bring certain matters before the meeting. Our first and most important order of business is to elect eight directors for the coming year. All of the nominees are members of the present Board of Directors." Acting like a man in a hurry, he then read their names and made it clear every one of them had already been overwhelmingly re-elected by proxy vote, tabulated by an IBM machine.

Mrs. Stephens, no woman to be intimidated by automation, got up from her seat on the front row and inquired whether there might be discussion.

Waving his hand impatiently, the president bade the lady have her say. Curiosity showed through his impatience.

"One question," she said succinctly, already knowing the

answer. "How much stock in Castlerock, if any, do the members of the Board of Directors own?"

Mr. Feegle narrowed his eyes and wiggled his jaw muscles.

At length he replied curtly, "I do not have the slightest idea."

The little theater became filled with restive noises. The stockholders did not care for their president's attitude.

Mrs. Stephens went on blandly. "As stockholders," she turned and waved grandly over her bereaved sisters, "we must press for an answer to my question." As one, fourteen black hats and veils nodded in unison.

Mr. Feegle stared briefly, then turned to consult a smooth Madison Avenue specimen that Jane took to be his public relations director. Gratified, the president turned and said to Mrs. Stephens, "We do not consider the question within the purview of our interests."

Mrs. Stephens snapped, "Well, it is within the purview of *our* interest. My question is entirely proper. We strongly feel that the board members should own stock in any companies they pretend to represent. Only then are they truly, personally identified with profits."

Recognizing a militant adversary, Mr. Feegle decided it was wise to shift gears. He replied, "Four of the eight directors have owned some 56,000 shares of common. They have disposed of 50,000 shares, however, during the past two years."

"Would you explain why?" Mrs. Stephens calmly asked.

"Personal reasons," barked Mr. Feegle. "Purely personal, private reasons." He began drumming on the podium with all ten fingers.

Mrs. Stephens, still standing, leaned over to consult with Miss Green. Then she straightened and replied, "We do not consider your reply adequate."

Mr. Feegle's calm blew to smithereens. "Is a company on the skids to Hell," he yelled, "just because a director sells his stock?"

"You did not say whether the other four directors have owned stock in Castlerock." Mrs. Stephens was being so exasperatingly even-voiced that Jane had an idiotic seizure. She wanted to help rescue Mr. Feegle, who by now was perspiring freely.

"Four directors own no stock!" he shouted. "Never have! Not a damn share!"

His big mistake was in shouting at the lady, and in cursing, for Mrs. Stephens had kept both her dignity and her calm. Consequently, when she sat down, her mission accomplished, the little crowd of stockholders let off spontaneous steam. There were whistles, hoots, a few shouts of "Give 'em hell!"

Then, very formally, a stockholder in the sixth row stood up. A handsome, lanky Texan—his accent was unmistakable, as was the 10-gallon hat in his hand—he spoke reproachfully, "Well, now, suh, I see little cause for swearing at a nice lady. Besides, I long been in accord with the good lady's principle, so stated. No director in any company has any business servin' less he knows, from the inside his skin on out, what that company means to the stockholdah dollahs."

Mrs. Hope was beside herself. "A man from God's own country!" she hollered. Standing up, she waved to the Texan, which encouraged him to keep up the good work. In all modesty and just for the record, he added, "I'm speakin' for 10,000 shares of common and 2,000 preferred, accumulated over a period of 30 years."

"Isn't he wonderful," gasped Mrs. Hope.

Even the Madison Avenue boys were impressed; they pulled Mr. Feegle back for a brief word.

Like a robot, Mr. Feegle then recited, "We are most impressed with the proposal of stock ownership as requirement for a company directorship. Your company will take appropriate action."

Having given in with what he believed to be infinite grace, Mr. Feegle moved on to a warming finale. "Your company," he began uctuously, "is working for your interests, and we are all delighted to have an expression thereof." There were additional platitudes, which became more and more beclouded. "The road from Castlerock," he reported, "stretches into every byway of this great country, and behind our success stands management's emphasis on diversification and research. Castlerock can be likened unto the mighty oak, whose strong roots go deep in their continuing search for new sources of nourishment, new strength, new horizons. Castlerock creates products for your rest, your daily health, your leisure time, your convenience, your enjoyment. Castlerock mattresses are in use in virtually every civilized nation. Castlerock chemical toilets are on the farms, on the waterways, in the skies. For your own pleasure and information, Castlerock Cameras are recording memorable intimacies in the lives of loved ones."

This last sentiment obviously went a little farther than Mr. Feegle had intended, and the outbreak of sniggers flustered him. Angry anyway, he ended curtly, "Our officers will mail you a report of today's proceedings." He looked around at his lieutenants, snapped his fingers, and they arose as one for adjournment.

This was a sad tactical error, a woeful underestimation of the power of a woman. At a signal from her president, Mrs. Hayden-Critchfield rose to her full willowy height and in the tones of Lady Macbeth made the theater vibrate with her indignation.

"We are by no means ready to adjourn the meeting! It should be adjourned only at the pleasure of the stockholders here assembled."

From her seventy-five fellow stockholders came incredulous gasps, then applause, and more cries of "Give 'em hell!" which Mrs. Hayden-Critchfield turned to acknowledge with a professional bow. As she did so the officers on the stage sat down again, like sacks of potatoes falling into place, while Mr. Feegle stood, his hand on his forehead, as if shielding a sudden migraine.

It was Jane's turn; like a jack-in-the-box she popped up as Mrs. Hayden-Critchfield sat down.

"As the president of the Golden Girls of the West, San Francisco investment club," she began, "it is my sad duty to report that we appear here today in mourning for our lost dividend."

Now the crowd, swept along by the spirit of the thing, began to clap and stomp and roar its approval. "Hot damn!" somebody shouted, and above everybody else the Teaxn cut loose at the top of his lungs with the rebel yell, "Ya-hoo!"

A hearty, happy female voice from the front row echoed the rebel yell. It was a Texan moment.

The Golden Girls' president held up her hand for silence. It was a full minute in coming. Everybody felt too good.

"The lost dividend has not been explained," she reminded Mr. Feegle.

"How about it?" a chorus behind Jane pressed the question. One man yelled, "Out with it, prexy."

Snapped Mr. Feegle, "The cost of research. Routine business. Soft market."

Jane waited for him to say more, but he had spoken his all on the subject. Unaccustomed to arrogance, she tried another tack. "We understand that executive compensations have been substantially increased within the past few months."

Mr. Feegle stood before the podium glaring, his arms folded. He said nothing. Becoming unnerved, Jane gamely plunged on, hoping that the waver in her voice did not show. Referring to her notes helped; they were props.

"Has the president," she asked, "taken a cut in his $200,000 salary, plus bonuses, until such time as dividends can be reinstated? Moreover, do the company's six ex-presidents and two ex-chairmen of the Board still receive some $998,253.51 in annual compensation? Or have they agreed to an adjustment until such time as the stockholders' needs are met?"

Conscious of a big moment, the audience was deathly still, and as Jane sat down she fought a surging impulse. The courageous crusade for all stockholders everywhere was threatened by the impulse to tears of outrage.

Deciding on diversionary tactics, Mr. Feegle plunged. "First let me make an observation about your investment club. We at Castlerock do not appreciate being made mock of by shareholders, whom we try to please."

The Texan, for one, wasn't having any nonsense. "Answer the lady's question," he yelled. He had listened to Jane with awe and admiration. "Where do the stockholders come in?"

A loud male voice echoed, "Yeah! What about us?"

Mr. Feegle banged his fist on the podium. "The lady's questions are without relevance." Then, cornered, he again made the mistake of shouting and swearing. "She wants answers to matters that are none of her damn business! This company is run by its officers—experienced, well-qualified!" His voice rasped across Jane's cheek, and quite involuntarily she shivered.

On her feet like a shot, Miss Green asked for the floor.

Mr. Feegle's voice was an icicle."I have had enough of this preposterous spectacle." He whirled to walk off the stage.

"You can't do that, you big boob!" It was Mrs. Hope shrieking. Miss Green wanted to clobber her.

Instead, Miss Green began reciting corporate law, chapter and verse. Some men on the stage heard her formidable words only too well, and a vice-president hastily plucked at Mr. Feegle's sleeve to bid him listen. But the president brushed him off, closed his ears to the lawyer.

The little theater was in pandemonium. The Texan was yelling, the girls were bobbing up to say something and then sitting down again, the spectators were shuffling in their seats with pent-up anger. The loud male voice again shouted—this time, "Off with their heads!" This brought wild applause.

Jane wished she had never heard of such an ogre as Pim M. W. Feegle.

Then suddenly from the back of the theater boomed a rich, scholarly familiar voice. Recognizing it, Jane let out a little yell herself and began pounding Mrs. Hayden-Critchfield on the knee. The voice addressed Mr. Feegle and it said crisply, "Sir, it is clear that you are not familiar with corporate law, or else are choosing to ignore it. Either would be a serious mistake. May I remind you that you are in the employ of your stockholders, including the ladies whose questions you decline to answer."

Mr. Ernst! The authority with which he spoke silenced everybody utterly. Jane looked back at him and saw Lochinvar, Galahad, George Washington, and Bernard Baruch, all in one.

Mr. Ernst continued, "The ladies' investment club has among its members a distinguished corporation lawyer. It is possible you may want to consult her about this point." Then he added a whipper designed to fell an ox. "Provided, of course, she would be generous enough to overlook your unacceptable conduct."

"Ya-hoo!" went the rebel yell.

"Ya-hoo!" echoed a female voice.

Mr. Feegle looked like a man who ached to drop dead. It helped not at all that he was afraid he recognized the dean of San Francisco's financial community, and when a board member quickly passed him a note, he knew for sure he was in trouble.

This was not good for Mr. Feegle and Castlerock, not good at all. But things were looking up for Castlerock's stockholders. Perhaps even, as the girls believed, for stockholders everywhere.

Upon leaving the little theater Mrs. Hope collared the Texan before he knew what had hit him. "Where in Texas?" she asked, as if her life depended on his answer.

"Dallas." He grinned and held out his hand. "That all right with you?"

Within seconds the two were stepping into his lavender Cadillac, parked right in front in a no-parking zone.

Mr. Ernst was waiting out in front of the theater for Jane and the girls. And it just happened—one of those things. Mrs.

Hayden-Critchfield threw her arms around him and kissed him first. "Our hero!" she cried. And, well, since Jane knew her friend had never even met August Ernst before, she concluded it would look unfeeling and standoffish if she didn't do the same.

She also agreed to let the girls go on their way without her while she drove to the Sheraton Palace with Mr. Ernst. Later, at lunch in the Palm Court, he grinned and explained. "I went just for the show. But I couldn't take it when he attacked you!"

# TWENTY

~~~~~~~~~~~~~~~~~~~~~~~~~~~~~~~~~~~~~~~~~~~~~

Poor Wally was languishing in jail. Miss Green called Jane on a Friday afternoon to tell her all about it. Wally had flown in from Edmondton, Canada, only the night before, had been arrested at 9:07 that morning, and immediately consigned to the county jail. The Grand Jury would ponder the case Monday evening—or in only four more days—and at that time either free him with a pat on the back or, as Miss Green put it so very legally, "further detain him with an indictment." Of course, the Golden Girls would have to appear at the hearing.

"I'm getting terribly curious about Wally's defense," Miss Green said. "He didn't go to Canada just to do a little fishing. And surprisingly, his firm has engaged the best defense man on the Coast."

It was now four o'clock, and until Miss Green's call had shattered her, Jane had been contentedly pressing her lovely Italian silk suit and thinking about August Ernst, who was dropping by at 6 o'clock.

With her heart aching for Wally, and her mind hoping that his defense would confound them all, Jane went to her desk and tried writing him a note. But what does one say to a friend one has helped lodge behind bars? Nothing even halfway sensible would come; Jane found herself unable to improve the situation. Finally she crumpled the piece of note paper and threw it to Kim to bat around.

Turning to the possible, she called Mrs. Hope and asked her to notify the girls of the Grand Jury hearing. Then, as if she alone were responsible, she admitted that Wally was already in jail.

"My God! My God! That poor dear boy!" There was a gulp and a moment's pause and then Mrs. Hope became practical. "We'll get him a Texas lawyer. Texas lawyers have so much more experience with crooks, really big ones—and they're *all* out free. I'll call a lawyer friend in Dallas right away."

Since meeting Rhett Crockett at the Castlerock shareholders' meeting, now ten days ago, Mrs. Hope had reverted to being hopelessly, militantly Texan—a situation more likely to become worse than better since Rhett, after driving off to Dallas, had promptly flown right back in his Cessna to spend two days with her in Carmel. Her reversion to "Texanism" had been at the expense of California, which she now openly considered to be a dinky, garish, small-bore place peopled by shallow thinkers.

Now, with Jane's warm reassurance about Wally's lawyer, Mrs. Hope's flighty thoughts suddenly departed Wally altogether and, out of the blue, she asked Jane to go with her to Acapulco for Christmas. "The *Lurline* has the smartest cruise over the holidays," she explained. "It's called the widow's cruise because practically everybody on it is hunting somebody new. You know. People who already have somebody don't go sailing around at Christmas time. Besides, we'll have our money from the Countess by then. We ought to do something terrific."

All this sounded quite daring to Jane, but she quickly declined. Her mind could not hurdle Wally, and she was in no mood to be gay. Then her friend began to plead. "Rhett just loves to travel and *he's* going if his daughter has her baby by that time." She'd already told Jane that Rhett was a widower.

"Think what fun!" and then Mrs. Hope plunged into a woman-to-woman confidence. "I'm playing hard to get," she said. "And he's so lousy rich he's being cagey. But I could just tell him you're dying to go and need somebody to go with. Then he wouldn't feel trapped. I'd just be humoring *you*. See?"

Jane did see. Smiling slowly to herself, she promised Mrs. Hope to think about it.

Having dinner with Mr. Ernst that evening, Jane told him about Wally, and finished off brightly, "You know, I think when this whole dreadful thing is over I'll take the Christmas cruise to Acapulco." Two seconds before this popped out, nothing was farther from Jane's thoughts than Acapulco, unless it was Tibet, or so she thought. But Mrs. Hope had dangled an extra lure; she'd called right back to urge Jane to let her old teammate pay her way, and this friendly gesture had set off a whole series of unfamiliar emotions in Jane.

Mr. Ernst thought Acapulco such a capital idea that he called the waiter and ordered champagne. They were dining at Ernie's, a rich textured restaurant all done with dark red walls and crystal chandeliers.

As she told Mr. Ernst about her friend's generous offer, she went on thoughtfully, "But I can't let her, of course. It's so astonishing I can hardly realize it, but even if I get nothing from the Countess, I'll be able—" Unexpectedly choked by emotion, she paused to recover a better balance. The thought of being able to afford such extravagance was something she would have to become accustomed to slowly, ever so slowly.

August Ernst looked fondly at his dinner companion, then reached out his hand and closed it over hers. "I know precisely. Lone Star reached 215 today, and with two hundred shares—" He pressed her hand. "Dazzling. Absolutely dazzling. From $3200 to $43,000!"

Jane nodded, but her mind was on something more important than money.

"Yes," Mr. Ernst went on, catching her mood and leaning toward her in a triumph of understanding. "You are financially

independent and a free woman! You can go to Acapulco under
your own steam!"

"Yes!" said Jane fervently. "Yes!" How wonderful that he
understood how important this was!

The champagne came and Mr. Ernst raised his glass. He said,
"I'd love to toast a charming companion. But tonight let's both
drink to the stock market. You because it gave you independence.
And I because it brought us together."

As they sipped their drinks Jane's emotions suddenly knew the
answer to a question her mind had frankly asked. Yes, the cer-
tainty came in a great burst of feeling that rushed through her
body in a glorious sweep of prescience. With all her being she
knew she owned the capacity to love again. This admirable man.
This dear companion. . . . What was he saying?

He was saying with enthusiasm, "Look, Jane. It's a gorgeous
trip. Promise me you'll go." His eyes were so full of pleading—
it seemed, for some reason, so vitally important to him—that she
finally said, "I will. Yes, I'll go!"

When she got home that night she called Mrs. Hope and said
cheerfully, "Let's go!"

Mrs. Hope, delighted, yelped, "Well, as a favor to you!" She
promised to make reservations right away.

Saturday noon, Mrs. Hope took a cab to San Francisco's huge
Hall of Justice, which contains the county jail, and just as she
was tipping the cabbie a brilliant idea struck. Hence, before
going in, she quickly walked the hundred yards down an alley-
way to one of San Francisco's smartest restaurants, the Blue Fox.
It was directly opposite the city morgue, at the rear of the Hall of
Justice.

Going into the Blue Fox, Mrs. Hope ordered dinners for
three nights, to be delivered to a Mr. Wallace Googins, in care
of the jail of the County of San Francisco; and, being a woman

of the world, she gave the address as if it were the presidential suite of the Mark Hopkins. Really putting her mind to it, she specified Boned Jumbo Squab *sous cloche, avec* wild rice, Filet Mignon, and Frog Legs with Artichoke bottoms in Sauce Blue Fox. For Wally's three desserts she ordered cherries jubilee, fried cream and *crêpes suzettes.*

"With each dinner," she said, "send along a proper wine of your own choosing." Then she left her Hilton Carte Blanche, picked up her package and her magazines, walked across the alley and took the elevator up to the jail, which was on the third floor. Three dinners would be sufficient, she thought with pleasure. By then it would be Monday and the Grand Jury would apologize to Wally and let him go.

The elevator deposited her directly opposite a barred door, and by peering down a long corridor she could make out a brilliantly lighted room filled with stern men in khaki. "The Gestapo," she muttered to herself. Nevertheless, as she rang the bell for admittance, she determined to remain cool and collected. Mrs. Hope fancied she had a way with petty officials.

A khaki-clad Storm Trooper with a revolver in his holster admitted her by turning a grotesque key six inches long. It prompted her to say pleasantly, "I have come to see the Count of Monte Cristo."

The jailer didn't get it. Nevertheless, he silently led her into the office and turned her over to a steel-jawed, well-holstered officer standing behind a long counter. Bored, he looked at her vacantly. Mrs. Hope gave it another try, with a brightly different tack. "I'm the Countess of Monte Cristo," she said flirtatiously. "I have brought the Count some shirts, an electric razor, and some magazines. Also, a television set will be delivered this afternoon."

Steel-Jaw, who was bespectacled and bald-headed, permitted his mouth to slack while he stared at her over the top of his glasses. Finally he beckoned to two fellow officers lounging at the end of the counter.

"Men," he asked, "have we got a count in here?"

The men drifted nearer. The first one, pleased with his wit, replied, "The place is full of no-counts."

The other, going along, said, "Sure. We've got counts. We also got dukes, princes, and a Napoleon or two on his way to Vacaville."

Deciding her joke had become soggy, Mrs. Hope became brisk.

"I'm having a television set sent in this afternoon," she repeated. "Will you please see that it's delivered to Mr. Wallace Googins?" Then she informed them that Mr. Googins' dinners would be delivered at seven and warned them against letting them grow cold. "Now will somebody please show me to his room?"

The khaki trio burst out with guffaws so loud that Mrs. Hope jumped. Finally Steel-Jaw said sadly, "Countess, this is not the Waldorf." He patiently explained that a prisoner could not receive a television, a razor, shirts, dinners, or a lady—especially not a lady.

"Now, look here!" Mrs. Hope fired straight. "In Texas a friend of mine was in jail with a TV, a case of bourbon, even a refrigerator for his ice. And they let 'im have all the lady visitors he wanted. So there!"

Steel-Jaw, now grinning broadly, said, "Don't tell me nobody thought to give him a contour chair." He made tut-tut noises over such carelessness.

Mrs. Hope merely fumed.

Bored by now, Steel-Jaw suggested, "You'd better join the ladies waiting to see this same prisoner." Then he blurted. "Say, who is this guy? Elvis Presley? Frankie Sinatra?" Immediately regretting his impertinent questions, he simmered down. "You can see 'im during visitin' hours, beginnin' at one o'clock. I'll show you where to wait."

mission that she had lent Wally $250 toward the down payment on his car.

"Oh, he was so cute about taking it," she hastened to add. "And when he came to pay it back he brought the sweetest little daphne for my garden. Such an understanding, thoughtful boy."

Not one to let Mrs. Stephens get ahead of her, Mrs. Hayden-Critchfield forced a laugh and said, "Oh, my dears, you should have seen Wally fill in when Henry had to fly to Chicago just before our last party. You'd all be amazed at his perfect elegance."

She had injected a surprisingly domestic touch which none of the girls save Mrs. Hope could begin to compete with. But Mrs. Hope, taking one look around to see whether she dared tell about her weekend with Wally in Carmel, decided that judgment should stay her tongue. Or perhaps it was Mrs. MacKinnon's presence. Not able to resist completely, however, she offered in an intimate tone, "Wally just adores making people happy." It was a remark no one could quarrel with, not even a rival, and Mrs. Hope was dreamily content to let Helen Spalding take her turn.

Mrs. Spalding spoke slowly and lugubriously, as if they were attending Wally's wake. "He had a very complex character. He was an angry young man, to be sure. But so much more than that. So much more." Eschewing competitive details, Mrs. Spalding, the writer, knew the power of leaving things to the imagination.

Now the psychologist came up with a sage nugget that made everybody even more snappish. After all, it did seem to be true. "Wally is a different man," she said, "to every woman he knows."

The girls were mulling this over when the door opened and Steel-Jaw announced, "It's one o'clock, ladies. Two ladies at a time."

Since Mrs. Hope and Mrs. Hayden-Critchfield were nearest to the door, Steel-Jaw beckoned to them and they followed him back to the counter where he confiscated their packages and magazines—Mrs. Hayden-Critchfield's transistor radio and copies of the *New Yorker* and *True*. Mrs. Hope's carton of Marlboros and copies of *Mad* and *Sports Cars Illustrated*. Sullenly, they followed their guide through a steel door that groaned open to his monstrous key. Once inside a large windowless room, he waved them toward a dense, practically opaque screen wall, squinted through the screen with his nose up close and said, "The Count will be here shortly." Strong lights from above glared down upon the screen.

Moving closer, the two girls, by shielding their eyes and squinting, could finally make out the form of a tall, slender young man hurrying toward them. His shoulders were erect, his step eager. Wally's denims might be faded but his spirits were not, and when he could see the girls from his side of the screen he let out a whoop. "My girls! My victims! My persecutors!" he cried. "My God, it's wonderful to see you!"

"Ten minutes," snapped old Steel-Jaw, looking at his watch. Then he decently walked away. "Crackpots," he muttered to himself.

All the girls dreaded the Grand Jury hearing. Their awe was bad enough; and they were humiliated to parade their own pathetic gullibility. Even so, their president observed, the biggest problem was their jealousy. The unhappy undertones troubled Jane deeply.

Yet, afterwards, she was extremely thankful that things had happened exactly as they had, for a threatening situation had cleared rapidly and quite unexpectedly—thanks solely to Steel-Jaw.

Forgetting that Wally was in prison not for violence but for art, Steel-Jaw had absentmindedly slipped him into handcuffs and marched him into the hearing. Or, if Steel-Jaw hadn't simply forgotten, he had reached the mature conclusion that any young man with so many middle-aged female followers was a potential Blue Beard. In any case, the effect of the steel shackles upon the girls had been electric. One look at Wally and Mrs. Stephens had bounded out of her seat and cried, "What a shameful thing to do—to try and influence the jury!" Mrs. Hope had shouted to the District Attorney, "Take those things off that boy instantly. Do you hear me? California is sick, sick, sick!"

Frankly embarrassed over the guard's boner, the District Attorney had curtly ordered Wally freed of his manacles. But the hardware, not to mention the Grand Jury's prompt indictment, had nonetheless proved a felicitous turning point. That is, in Jane's opinion, considering everything. For the searing wave of indignation that swept through the Golden Girls burned away their petty jealousies and released their fighting spirit of all-for-one-and-one-for-all. Jane could feel it and even see it happen as the proceedings had moved forward: the girls, seated on the front row, had begun sitting closer together, with elbows touching elbows for reassurance, and they had begun whispering to each other.

Their mood had changed so swiftly, in fact, that the president became apprehensive, and at one point it had taken all her tact to break up a conference between Mrs. Hope and Mrs. Hayden-Critchfield, a conference leading to a proposal to the District Attorney that Wally immediately be freed and placed in their joint custody on a share-and-share alike basis.

"No, no!" Jane had whispered frantically. "Don't be impulsive."

Despite her anxiety about the over-enthusiasm, however, she thrilled to the change. For she now knew that Wally, at his trial, would have the united, unquestioning support of the Golden Girls. She also knew that it would test all her wisdom to harness this lively force and direct it meaningfully in his behalf.

Studying the implications, Jane didn't know just how she could do this. It was a problem she'd have to work out most thoughtfully. But that she might *not* be able to do anything never really entered her head.

Wally was indicted on two counts—Grand Theft and violation

of California's Corporate Securities Act—just as Miss Green had predicted. Trial was set for December 1, six weeks away. Meantime, his own firm bailed him out; and the $10,000 bail, in view his clients' losses of $35,000, was considered reasonable.

Wally went through the motions of carrying on as usual for Van Dyke and Buchanan. But that was the only usual thing about him these weeks. While he kept his spirit, he had no taste left for asserting his independence. Every evening he spent with Eleanor.

Jane caught only fleeting glimpses of him as he came and went to Eleanor's apartment. She made no effort to avoid him nor to break into his shell of aloofness. Miss Green had made it most emphatic that the girls were not to see Wally "socially" until after the trial.

But one Sunday noon at the Bonelli's, where the old foursome had gathered for lunch, Jane learned more about Wally than she had ever known before. And about Eleanor, too, for that matter.

The conversation had begun casually enough when Al mentioned Jane's new independence and her trip to Acapulco.

It was Eleanor who said, toying with a slice of melon, "Just what is independence? Wally used to brag about his. But now he says, 'Any bum on Skid Row has plenty of independence, but what can he do with it? Independence doesn't mean anything unless you have freedom of action!'"

Jane noted to herself, with as much satisfaction as she could feel under the circumstances, that trouble is a great leveler. It had made Wally Googins, that free spirit, a subscriber to homilies.

Eleanor, needing to talk, went on. "I didn't buy a single share of Canadian Countess, but I'm worse off than all the Golden Girls put together. All they can lose is money. I can lose everything." Tears welled in her eyes.

Rosemarie looked at her with special tenderness. "You mean—you and Wally? Really?"

Eleanor nodded. "It sounds so strange to hear yourself saying it. But I'm hopelessly in love with the guy."

"I thought so," said Rosemarie gently. "I've thought so all along."

Eleanor began to cry softly and Jane, her own eyes blinking hard, reached out, circled Eleanor's shoulders, and asked soothingly, "How long have you known, dear?"

"Since last summer, when Phil Petry asked me to marry him. I knew then it was Wally." She went on haltingly. "Oh, last summer was so ghastly. Wally stayed away. Then during all the time he was in Canada he never even let me know where he was. When he came home he just said he'd been fighting himself all the time."

"I wonder what he meant by that?" Al asked her.

"He meant he didn't know whether he ought to see me again. He didn't know for sure whether he had the right."

"Did he say that—really?" Al was thoughtful for a long moment. "The poor guy!"

"Now that he's back he says he's positive—he wants to get married right after the trial."

"Even—even if well, you know." Al didn't know how to ask it; some things are impossible to put just right. To his amazement, he suddenly saw Wally in a new light; he was almost on his side. "Did he tell you the whole story about Canadian Countess?"

"Oh," cried Eleanor, "he swears that everything will be all right now—new management or something. He keeps saying it's solid now, but that every day counts." Clearly, Eleanor, youngest and prettiest of his victims, believed in Wally, as they all had. "What can I *do*?" she asked.

Jane patted her shoulder. "There's nothing, my dear, that you *can* do now. We'll just have to wait—and not lose hope." Yes, she who had started it all had an obligation to them both. Her mind flew back to the emotions she had felt when she first invested Eleanor's $300 in the market, but this paled in the light of her present responsibility. She would do anything, anything on earth, to help them now.

As usual, when Jane needed an answer, she consulted primary sources, and in the few weeks left before the trial she read miles of testimony of criminal cases similar to Wally's. But nothing she read did any good, since the mumbo-jumbo of the law was even more obscure than that of the stock market. Jane's parade of witnesses added up to nothing.

Then one evening when she told herself she faced a stone wall as solid as San Quentin's, an idea hit her with stunning force. Maybe it wasn't *what* all these witnesses said that was so important. Maybe the *way* they said it was important too.

At least, Jane now had the core of an idea for saving Wally from damaging testimony.

But first, she would have to try it out on the girls. They would either take to it or they wouldn't, and she couldn't push, for her idea *was* daring. Maybe, she reflected, it was even the least shade illegal.

# TWENTY-ONE

In Superior Court Number Nine, at 9:45 on the morning of December 1, the atmosphere was heady with suspense as the principals assembled against the hour of ten. The people of the State of California were settling in to assess the havoc wrought by one Wallace Abner Googins.

Two of the people—small ones—were walking hand-in-hand along the marble corridor leading to the courtroom. The elder, who had no sound reason for happiness, had a hopeful lift to her chin and a certain gleam in her eyes. Her companion, a sweet-faced girl of twenty-two, was suspiciously red-eyed from weeping.

Jane squeezed Eleanor's hand. Having tried everything else, she now tried the long view, the historical perspective. "We must just be calm, dear," she told Eleanor. "All through the ages women have suffered with their men for their follies. They have had to bind up their wounds and bring them home and comfort them as best they could. It's one of the great themes of literature."

"But what if they don't let me bring Wally home?"

The question was a reasonable one, and Jane decided not to try answering directly. "Let us not be defeatist," she said. "Let's not underestimate the power of sixteen—ah, fifteen—women, all working toward a common goal."

"I'm terrified your idea won't work," Eleanor said. "Isn't there some way the district attorney can *make* you talk?"

"Oh, we'll all talk, dear," Jane assured her. "It's just that there's no way to force the jury to *hear*."

190

Vasiliu

Arriving at the door of the courtroom itself, the two paused to get their bearings. The Golden Girls were already there, sitting in the first three rows directly in front of the bar of justice. Miss Green and Mrs. Hope, in the front row, were saving a seat for their president between them. Wally was to their left, at a small table, shoulder-to-shoulder with his attorney. Both looked up when Jane and Eleanor walked in and both smiled serenely. Wally waved reassuringly to Eleanor; bravely, she forced a wan little smile in return. She took a seat directly behind Jane.

The president of the Golden Girls seated herself, exchanged dignified nods of greeting with her members, thrust one hand in back of her for Eleanor to grasp, crossed the fingers of her other hand, and waited for proceedings to begin. She had done her mortal best. But complete serenity would not come. Brilliant as the results of yesterday's meeting had been, there was still room for doubt, still a chance of failure.

Yesterday, the girls had all gathered for lunch at Mrs. Hayden-Critchfield's home. Jane had called a special meeting for Miss Green, who wanted to coach them as prospective witnesses. After fresh crab salad and hot biscuits, their attorney had given quite a brisk little talk.

"Answer every question firmly and whenever possible with a simple 'Yes' or 'No.' And remember," she emphasized, "do remember to tell the absolute truth." Then, on the practical level, she had advised the girls to avoid getting all gussied up for the trial. "Especially avoid wearing expensive furs and jewelry," she had said, and there were quite a few words about how impressionable jurors are. "If you want your money back, you should look as if you really need it."

"We get you," Mrs. Hope had nodded. "Poor and hungry."

Miss Green had hurried bark to her office, and it was while

the girls lingered over their coffee that Jane had taken over the meeting. And introduced her Idea.

"It's really a shame Gertrude had to rush to an appointment," she began, knowing full well that Gertrude would turn purple at what she was about to say.

Picking her words carefully, she gave the members an account of her reading in the Hastings Law School Library. Then she casually observed that she had noted a perfectly remarkable detail in her research. "I observed again and again," she said, "that witnesses who cannot be *heard* well cannot really be effective. In other words, they cannot really harm the defendant."

Piquing the girls' curiosity, she had gone on calmly enough, despite her fluttering emotions. "Female voices," she had noted, "are particularly hard to hear in a large room. Which, of course, I have always noticed in classrooms, too." Jane had thrown in her observations about classrooms to make her point as general as it could be made, which made her feel less conspiratorial. And now, having gone this far, she had to plunge on.

"I noticed in my reading of testimony that attorneys often had to beg *women* witnesses to speak up more loudly. And the harder the women were to hear, the fewer the questions they were asked. In fact, it was really fantastic."

"I get it!" Mrs. Hayden-Critchfield gleefully interrupted. "We could use the old Lysistrata technique. You know, lie down on the job—do a fade-out on really critical questions!"

"Well. . . ." said the president. Excited with such pupil response, she felt utterly lawless and the sensation, while novel, was faintly disturbing.

Mrs. Hayden-Critchfield was now on her feet. "Suppose I give a demonstration of the possibilities," she said eagerly.

Intimidated by her own daring, the president could only nod approval.

The demonstrator faced the girls and they watched intently

as she put her hand to her throat. "You can open your mouth, move your lips perfectly, without making a single sound!"

Jane wanted to point out complete muteness was hardly required, but a good teacher knows better than to hold back on pupil enthusiasm. Besides, the girls loved the idea and thought the possibilities simply hilarious—especially when the actress announced she would run through a bit of *The Cremation of Sam McGee*. And she did, with obvious eloquence and stunning silence. The girls had to clap.

Helen Spalding observed, "It's like when the sound dies on TV."

Giving a professional warning that the labials were easier to control than the fricatives, Mrs. Hayden-Critchfield put the girls through five minutes of practice. Except for a few chirps, a giggle or two and one *Merde*," they all did beautifully. Sometimes they merely sounded faint, sometimes they blanked clear out. Glowing with satisfaction, their teacher turned the class back to the president and resumed her seat.

With grave dignity, the president thanked Mrs. Hayden-Critchfield in behalf of the class and then warned, "We must be careful not to overdo it, of course. It's just that we may have—for really critical moments a new and powerful tool to use in poor Wally's behalf."

Mrs. Stephens said, "Hope we won't look as if we've eaten alum."

Mrs. Hope observed wryly, "Be one hell of a note if the D. A. is a lip reader."

But nobody really worried about that.

The courtroom fell deadly silent when the District Attorney strode in, stern and businesslike. He settled at a large table, unzipped his briefcase, extracted a single exhibit, and placed it carefully in the center of the table.

Wally and Jane saw it at the same instant. It was Jane's notebook.

Wally looked at her, grinned crookedly, and sighed aloud, "My pen pal!"

Jane shivered a little at that, but managed a stoic smile.

The Honorable Timothy X. O'Malley, Judge, walked in while looking at his watch, a fat gold timepiece with a hinged cover which he snapped shut. He was a cadaverous, high-domed, elderly gentleman without a shred of hair. But the District Attorney compensated.

Representing the People was the Honorable C. Matthew Arnold, District Attorney. From the beginning, Jane had thought he looked like a werewolf, and he *was* hirsute. He had a great shock of red hair, close set eyes, and thick red eyebrows that turned up at the ends like harlequin spectacles.

"Egad," Mrs. Hope whispered to Jane. "In Texas we set the dogs on better lookin' men than that."

At this point Jane reminded her friend to take a tranquilizer.

Representing the Defendant was the Honorable Justin R. Tilly, a broad-shouldered man with a jut jaw, a quick eye and, Jane was glad to see, a tremendous store of confidence. He and Wally were conferring so cheerfully, and with such surprising enjoyment of their surroundings, that Jane made a mental note to retain Mr. Tilly if she ever ran afoul of the law.

Twelve citizens good and true were comfortably seated in the jury box, and in view of the defendant's personality Jane was gratified to see that nine of the twelve were women. Among the jury were a card punch operator, a pastry cook, a shipping clerk from Boy Scout Headquarters, a hotel maid, and a Christmas tree decorator.

At a signal from the bench, both attorneys squared off to declare themselves ready, the defendant's plea of Not Guilty was formally noted, the complainants were sworn in as a body, and as Jane's blood congealed slightly, Miss Green was asked to step forward as first witness.

Hoping to set a perfect example for the girls, Miss Green had asked the D.A. to take her first, and she *was* impressive. She answered briefly, in well-rounded tones, and most, most willingly. But since she had never purchased any Canadian Countess, her testimony was utterly useless to the prosecution.

Then it was Jane's turn, and Eleanor squeezed her hand.

Without an iota of warning, as she mounted the witness stand, she felt herself clamped in the paralysis of buck fever—not about taking the witness stand, which she did without a fumble, but about her Idea. She was a complete idiot who had given birth to an idiot notion. Her Big Idea indeed! To inject such impertinence into such sacred solemnity! The mere thought now made her go blank, and she looked at the menacing figure of the District Attorney as if she'd never seen him before. Yet he seemed to be talking to her, wanting to know something about her address or occupation. The District Attorney had to ask her a second time.

Then she caught sight of Eleanor, who was obviously praying hard, and of Mrs. Hope who winked at her, and the sight of her friends brought her back to reality. A trooper to the hilt, Mrs. Hope—her tangerine hair flying—had elected to wear a dismal black dress borrowed from her maid, along with cheap costume earrings that dangled and bracelets that clanked. Moreover, she was speaking to Jane now, with her lips forming silent words of encouragement. The girls were doing their part! Of course she had to do hers!

The District Attorney was saying to her, "I asked—do you know the defendant?"

"Yes, I do." Jane's voice was almost steady now.

"Under what circumstances did you first meet the defendant?"

"We were seatmates in an investment class. We were and are good friends."

"Just answer the question factually," warned the District Attorney.

Wally grinned at his lawyer, who appeared only slightly interested.

"Do you mean by that," asked the D.A., "that you shared the *same* seat on one of those old-fashioned double benches?"

Defense attorney objected. Question irrelevant. Objection sustained.

Frowning, the interrogator went on. "This class was in the city and county of San Francisco?"

"Yes."

The District Attorney began strutting a little, pacing back and forth in front of her. Jane imagined he was warming up. She tried to feel she was doing the same.

"Calling your attention to approximately October of last year, did you have occasion to talk with the defendant?"

"Yes." Jane was proud of remembering to keep her answers brief.

"Did the defendant mention to you a certain security by the name of Canadian Countess?"

"Yes."

"Now will you tell the court, as nearly as you can recall, exactly what the defendant told you about Canadian Countess." The red eyebrows seemed to bristle and turn up even more sharply at their ends.

Now was the moment, and Jane could almost feel as a tangible force the girls' support as she leaned forward to give proper emphasis to her words. Her eyes brightened with eagerness to tell her story and her lips formed words as she plunged ahead, rapid fire. But only a dim and toneless sound came out.

The District Attorney looked sharply at her, looked up at the Judge, who was not alert, said to his witness, "Will you repeat that—louder?"

She went through it again, this time adding gestures. But still her voice was too faint to be heard.

The District Attorney leaned toward her. "Will you speak louder, that the court may hear you?"

Smiling apologetically, Jane said distinctly, "I'm sorry. I shall try." She cleared her throat. "As I was saying . . ."

Her sound box shut off again, while the lips went on, and Jane became utterly fascinated that she had mastered this technique so well. In fact, she was smiling encouragement to the D.A. when he shut her off with a shout.

"Louder, louder—that the court may hear you!"

Stealing a look at the Judge, who was totally absorbed in examining the nail of his little finger, Jane murmured, "Sir, may I ask you to repeat the question?"

The District Attorney eyed her balefully, opened his mouth, glanced uneasily at the Judge and then closed his mouth. What with a Judge distracted by a torn nail, and with a difficult witness, he had forgotten his question. Finally he barked at the court reporter to read it. The reporter stood and read in a monotone.

"Now will you tell the court, as nearly as you can recall, exactly what the defendant told you about Canadian Countess?"

"Oh, yes, indeed." Deciding to address the jury directly, Jane thought she'd better speak firmly for a change. "Mr. Googins told me he was with Van Dyke and Buchanan, a firm interested in special situations. Many of them were wonderfully successful. I was impressed." Her voice trailed off, and nobody heard anything more.

The District Attorney, noting the Judge's yawn, quickly decided to change his pace. After all, he'd known this Judge to nod right off in open court. Walking to his table, he picked up Jane's notebook and addressed the Judge.

"Counsel has inspected this, your Honor. May I have this marked the People's Exhibit Number One for identification?"

The Judge nodded sagely. "It may be so marked." He promptly went back to his fingernail.

Turning back to Jane, the District Attorney begged, "Now, will you tell the court about your purchases of Canadian Countess?"

"Not purchases," Jane corrected him. "A single purchase."

"All right! But let's hear about it!"

"Well," she began, "what may I tell you about Canadian Countess?"

"How much was the amount of your purchase?"

"You mean in shares or dollars?"

"Shares!" thundered the D.A.

"Twelve thousand shares."

"And how much per share?"

"Twenty-five cents. And twelve thousand times twenty-five makes three thousand. Three thousand dollars."

"Thank you," said the D.A. At last the witness was cooperating. A little too encouraged by this evidence of his skill with difficult witnesses, he then asked a silly question. "You do have these certificates in safe keeping, say your safety deposit box."

"Oh, no, Sir! I keep them in coffee cans."

The D.A. stared. "In coffee cans?"

Jane heard Wally guffaw, and her girls tittered.

The Judge rapped. "Order in this courtroom!"

Jane nodded pleasantly at the Judge, then turned back to her inquisitor. "But they don't have coffee in them too."

"Oh, thank you for that information," said the D.A. icily. "I *am* grateful."

He looked at his watch, sighed, and then riffled through the notebook while Jane looked around. Miss Green, sitting like a ramrod, was flushed with professional vexation, but the other girls were smiling prideful encouragement and she blessed them for their loyalty. Wally's face was a study in complete amiability, while his attorney was trying to smother a grin. Eleanor was torn between worry and curiosity. The Judge's head was perilously close to falling on his chest.

"This *is* your notebook?" asked the District Attorney, handing it to her.

Jane examined it with the greatest care, finally admitted to owning the People's Exhibit Number One. Then, there being no escape, she identified Wally's comments on the Countess.

"That is all. Next witness, please." The District Attorney's face screwed up, as if from a shooting pain.

The witness returned to her seat and Mrs. Hayden-Critchfield took her place on the stand. She had given much thought to designing her own hat for just this occasion, and its motif was zealously appropriate. To suggest the wig of the English judge she had fashioned a rippling tiara of soft white ostrich feathers, tightly held by maline, and this pseudo-wig was topped by a tower of black velour, which in the creator's mind clearly connoted the Tower of London. The total effect, including the hat and a severely tailored Irene suit of black, worn with a white blouse, was quite arresting. So, too, was her performance. Appearing to be the world's most eager and conscientious witness, she could at no time be heard by the jury or by the Judge, but the latter—from sheer lack of communication—had by now fallen fast asleep anyway.

Taking her turn, Mrs. Hope—possibly because of the tranquilizer—worked her lips as if they were full of novocain. But Jane thought her satisfactorily exasperating.

So continued the trial of Wallace Abner Googins, as complainant after complainant did her best to serve the defendant; and the District Attorney wished he had never heard of either. Finally, goaded beyond endurance by tiny-voiced witnesses, he stomped to the bench and woke up the Judge.

"Your Honor, a number of witnesses are deliberately standing mute and I beg you to cite them for contempt of court!"

Jane felt her scalp tingle as she saw a look of exquisite satisfaction cross the face of Gertrude Green. But nothing came of the D.A.'s threat. To his obvious amazement, the Judge, who'd probably been dreaming, merely suggested that the Protector of the People call as his next witness the defendant himself. Slightly stunned, but too pleased to be rid of the girls to quibble, the District Attorney called Wally to the stand.

His attorney, however, slowly took to his feet. "Your Honor," he said, "my client respectfully declines to testify at this time."

At this Miss Green, completely capitulating to her admiration for legal processes, thawed and whispered to Jane, "A beautiful move! Wally really must have a defense!"

Disgusted, the District Attorney sat down heavily and waved his hand to turn proceedings over to Mr. Tilly. He bowed and invited the girls to be cross-examined. But since he had not heard enough to make such a ritual worthwhile, he soon gave up trying to make something of nothing. Besides, he wasn't interested. Jane and Mrs. Stephens were on for token appearances and that was all. With a wide smile Mr. Tilly waived the rest of the Golden Girls and called his own client to the stand.

Here, finally, was something to listen to. Wally spoke clearly, firmly, and followed the cues of his interrogator with a crispness that brought Miss Green forward in her seat and caused the Judge to ignore his fingernail. Deftly, Mr. Tilly took Wally through his recent trip to Canada.

"Will you tell the court exactly where you went in Canada recently?"

"Fort St. John and Edmonton."

"For how long?"

"For two weeks in Fort St. John, where I investigated the group of promoters who sold Canadian Countess. Then for eight days I was in Edmonton."

"And in Edmonton?"

"I was consulting with the Canadian correspondents of my own firm."

"Now will you tell us about the company known as Canadian Countess."

"Its business was originally petrochemicals. But some months ago, fortunately, it merged with a small company that produced natural gas. A wonderful little company."

"Objection!" The D.A. was having no salesmanship. Objection was sustained and Wally's last remark stricken from the record.

Mr. Tilly watched his timing carefully. "Is there presently a company known as Canadian Countess?"

"Oh, sure." Wally grinned broadly.

Jane, her heart skipping a few beats, looked around at Eleanor, who was frozen on the edge of her seat and clutching Jane's hand.

"And in what business at the present time?"

"Natural gas producers."

Mr. Tilly walked around for a minute, finally asked, off-handedly. "Did you yourself invest in this company?"

"Yes, sir! Four thousand dollars. All I had."

Slowly, in the typically tortured and impending manner of the law, Mr. Tilly pulled out the story of Canadian Countess, and as it spun out even the Judge was wide awake.

It was perfectly true that the Countess, as a producer of petrochemicals, had gone sour. "Poor management," Wally said. "Too many chiefs and not enough Indians." It was likewise true that the complainants had not been able last summer to sell their holdings. "Things were all fouled up last summer," Wally volunteered. "A mess."

"Could it be," then asked his counsel, "that in the beginning you demonstrated more courage than discretion, more enthusiasm than judgment?" This was safe enough; the attorney was purporting to show the jury that youth, inexperience and good faith are no sin.

Wally shivered. "Yes, sir! And that's something that'll never happen again!"

But what about the Countess now? The attorney adroitly got to the nubbin of the matter and brought out particulars—how the Countess had gone under new management, had switched to the production of natural gas; how, in fact, the merger had saved the parent company.

"And is Canadian Countess now actually taking out and marketing its natural gas?"

"Yes, *Sir,*" said Wally. "We're now taking just a modest fifty million cubic feet a day—to supply markets in Washington and Oregon. And California has huge markets opening up. In six months we'll be flowing in better quantity, and in a year. . . ."

"Objection!" shouted the D.A.

"Sustained," said the Court.

Mr. Tilly, happy enough, moved on to other lines of questioning. "Now when you were in Canada," he inquired, "what was the status of an investment in the company at that time?"

The girls were too excited to breathe. Mrs. Hope was clasping and unclasping her hands, which made her bracelets clank. Jane's lips were still busy forming soundless words.

Wally took full advantage of his moment. He slicked his hair, tugged at his dove-grey vest, and finally spoke.

"On my last trip to British Columbia, Canadian Countess was listed for the first time on the Toronto Stock Exchange. It's an up-and-coming company. An absolute bearcat."

"Objection!" shouted the District Attorney. One more time, Wally's editorial comments were stricken from the record.

"Just stick to the facts, please," warned Mr. Tilly.

After a second, Mr. Tilly went on. "And what was its listing price per share on that day, now about three months ago?"

"One-sixteenth of a cent, bid."

"Now, referring to the complaining witness who noted she purchased twelve thousand shares," Mr. Tilly went on. "At one-sixteenth of a cent per share, what would have been the value of her investment of three thousand dollars at that time?"

Jane gasped her surprise at Mr. Tilly's bold reference to her, then felt wildly frustrated without her slide rule. But Wally had been coached; he came up with the figures promptly.

"Seven dollars and fifty cents," he replied.

A ripple of laughter swept through the courtroom. The defending lawyer, pleased with himself, smiled upon his witness. Sensing something big about to happen, Miss Green leaned toward Jane and advised, "He's been setting us up. Now watch him!"

Pulling a telegram from his pocket, Mr. Tilly now addressed the court. "Your Honor, I desire at this time to produce Exhibit Number One, and the only exhibit, of the defendant. I identify it as a telegram received by me this morning at 8:43 o'clock from the secretariat of Canada's Royal Commission on Energy. With the court's permission, I shall read it into the record."

"So be it. Permission granted." All ears, the Judge leaned forward.

In a matter-of-fact voice, careful not to overplay, Mr. Tilly read his telegram. "At close of business on November 30, bid price of Canadian Countess on Toronto Stock Exchange quoted at one dollar ninety-one cents." Then, quite involuntarily, Mr. Tilly bowed. It was a great moment.

Mrs. Hope screamed, "Ya-hoo!"

Wally clasped his hands above his head like a prizefighter acknowledging victory and gave Eleanor and all the rest of his girls a brilliant smile. Eleanor burst into sobs of joy.

The Golden Girls began pummeling each other on the back and squealing all sorts of incredulous happy noises, and out of the corner of her eye Jane caught sight of two women on the jury who had most unlegal smiles on their faces.

"Order in the courtroom!" The Judge banged his gavel officiously, but there was no judicial frown on his face as Mr. Tilly, with a flourish, placed the telegram by the side of Jane's notebook.

Before turning his witness back to the District Attorney, Mr.

Tilly was determined to ice the cake. He asked Wally, "Referring once again to the complaining witness who purchased twelve thousand shares of Canadian Countess at a cost of three thousand dollars. Now will you tell us—what was the value of her investment at the close of yesterday's market?" The attorney handed his client a pen and an envelope to figure on.

Again, Jane ached for her slide rule.

Wally figured, then let out a low whistle.

With his case gone to hell anyway, and with half the jury whipping out pencil and paper and figuring too, the D.A. did not bother to object to Wally's low whistle.

Yet Wally answered formally, "At yesterday's market, twelve thousand shares of Canadian Countess would have brought twenty-two thousand nine hundred and twenty dollars." Now he looked toward Jane and on his face there was a smile containing the breadth of all happiness.

While Jane's emotions were trying to contain all that was so unexpectedly thrust upon her, including Wally's smile, Mrs. Hope was crying, "Now you can buy the whole damned *Lurline!*"

But the trial was not yet over.

For the People, Mr. C. Matthew Arnold had something to say. Quite sensibly, instead of querying his witness, he decided to put his remarks in the form of a little speech.

"We have witnessed here today a most unusual turn of events," he began. "I believe they point a lasting moral. They demonstrate the excessive risk of investing in a company that—ah, that, ah— which depends on luck. Pure luck. In brief, had this case been presented as late as one month ago, when I looked into the so-called 'bid' on Canadian Countess, I believe the defendant would have been found guilty on two—"

"OBJECTION!" shouted Mr. Tilly. "OUT OF ORDER! IRRELEVANT! INDEED, UNSEEMLY!"

"Objection sustained," observed the Judge, frowning at the District Attorney. "We are trying this case as of December 1."

In a matter of seconds now the jury filed out to reach its verdict, and Jane had not finished powdering her nose when it filed right back in again. The foreman, a truck driver, looked a little silly as he delivered the verdict. Wally and the complainants were already celebrating.

Afterwards, out in the marble corridor, Miss Green greatly relieved all the girls by walking off with the District Attorney.

They really had a bang-up time. They laughed, cried, shouted until the bailiff came to quiet them. Then Wally formed a receiving line of one in order to get to everybody coming by. Eleanor, a little overawed, shyly took her place at the end of the line. But Wally, seeing this, ran to get her, kissed her soundly, and proudly put his arm around her.

Then he announced, "My friends! This is Eleanor, my fiancée!" and Jane hugged them both.

The Golden Girls, ladies all, did the proper thing. They congratulated the happy couple. And if they had any reaction to Wally's suddenly producing a fiancée, it yielded quickly to a feeling of relief, a sudden realization that now, at least, everybody knew where everybody else stood. Then quietly, a little subdued, they began to drift away.

Jane, Eleanor and Wally were ready to leave at last when two lady jurors—who had been standing around—approached Wally and drew him aside.

"Sure thing!" Jane heard him say. "Sure, I'll get it for you! It'll be $10 by summer. Sister, this is just like buying AT and T at three cents!"

Looking up and catching sight of a faint smile on Jane's face, Wally grinned and added, "You might even call the Countess a 'baby blue chip.' "

# TWENTY-TWO

~~~~~~~~~~~~~~~~~~~~~~~~~~~~~~~~~~~~~~~~~~~

"I know a secret!" Mrs. Hope was teasing unmercifully. The two were on the telephone. But Jane didn't mind. Ever since the trial, three weeks ago now, she had been happy as the goose that laid the golden egg. There had been just two disappointments, one of which wasn't a disappointment at all, except to Al. Happy as Al was for Eleanor, he was still feeling let down for *himself* that Wally had turned out to be a good guy instead of a bad.

"Mighty discouraging," Al had admitted, grinning. "It's shot my confidence." To bolster his spirits, he'd already started plans for a big party to follow the wedding which would be right after the first of the year.

The real disappointment, however, was that August Ernst had called to say that he couldn't see Jane off on the *Lurline*. Regrettably, he was scheduled to be in Seattle on the day she sailed.

And that was tomorrow. The *Lurline* would sail at high noon. Mrs. Hope had reserved a stateroom on "A" deck. And Rhett Crockett's stateroom was right below, on "B" deck. Rhett had flown into town last evening and said he'd meet them on shipboard.

"But you won't be lonesome, honey," Mrs. Hope had assured her. "There'll be a hundred widowers to choose from."

Jane had bought new clothes from Ransohoff's and I. Magnin's and Saks Fifth Avenue, but she hoped her friend wouldn't leave her alone too much. The whole truth was—she now admitted it freely—she wasn't a whit interested in meeting anybody new, not after knowing August Ernst. She had even admitted to Rosemarie, "You know, I really can't wait to get home again!" Although she couldn't quite bring herself to say what she was really thinking, for it sounded over-young, what she meant was, "I don't want to go! I'll miss him too much!"

In the excitement of boarding the *Lurline,* however, Jane was glad she had come. After all, the trip was just for a few days; she had never been aboard a big liner, and she found the noise and confusion wonderfully exhilarating. Following a steward, she and Mrs. Hope finally made their way to their staterooms. Red roses were on the table.

"Rhett!" smiled Jane. "How lovely!"

But Mrs. Hope read the card and grinned broadly. "They're yours!"

They were from Mr. Ernst. His card said, "This is to say I shall really be with you for Christmas."

Jane couldn't understand why such a sweet sentiment was so comical, but Mrs. Hope laughed until she had to hold her sides. Then, still chuckling, she insisted that they hurry outside to see the *Lurline* as it put off. Besides, Rhett would be showing up.

They scurried along the decks until they reached the siderail where they took their stand, squeezing in among the other passengers, and began looking for the Golden Girls, who had all promised they'd come to wave goodbye. In fact, at one point the psychologist had even said she thought she might join Mrs. Hope and Jane and go along for the whole trip. It had been a mighty narrow escape.

An exciting show spread out below them. Mrs. Hope caught sight of Rhett getting out of a taxi and let out a "Ya-hoo" which, in view of all the noise, he could not hear.

Then Jane saw Mrs. Hayden-Critchfield pulling up with Miss Green and Mrs. Stephens in her Thunderbird, and they all began waving at the boat—just for the sake of waving—surely even before they saw Jane and Mrs. Hope.

But what made tears spring to Jane's eyes was the sight of Al's red Volkswagen chugging up to the dockside. And, piling out, were Al and Rosemarie, and then, from the back seat, Eleanor and Wally. And bless their dear hearts, Eleanor and Wally had brought Kim on a leash!

They finally spotted Jane and all began waving like crazy. Al, quite dazzling in a new green and gray sports coat, was smoking a cigar and strutting as if he owned the *Lurline*. Jane smiled through her tears as she saw him put his hand on Wally's shoulder to show him where to look for her. Then Wally, grinning, held up Kim and waved *his* paw.

"My God!" said Mrs. Hope. "You've got half of San Francisco seeing you off!"

A second later she said, "Look!" There, over to one side of the dock—a respectful distance from Eleanor and Wally—stood Helen Spalding and Phil Petry, arm in arm. They were laughing and waving, too.

Jane blew kisses while Mrs. Hope exclaimed, "*Do* you suppose?"

"Well," said Jane, "they're both so serious minded."

The *Lurline* blew its whistle—two shorts and a long—and a more thrilling sound Jane thought she had never heard.

But Mrs. Hope, oddly enough, seemed only to be trying to make herself heard above the sound and vibration—yelling in Jane's ear with a reckless disregard for her vocal cords. It was only when the noise abated for a moment that Jane could make out what she was saying.

"I've got a hot idea!" Mrs. Hope yelled. "When we get back let's have the Golden Girls give the Countess its first Award of Merit! My God, I'm a genius!"

Before Jane could weigh such an inspiration she saw Wally,

still holding Kim, suddenly act excited, say something to Eleanor, and point his finger at Jane.

Then Wally bent double with laughter. Whatever amused him, he had got Al and Rosemarie to look, too—pointing to Jane again. Now Al let out a whoop. Or least to Jane, watching intently, it looked like a whoop. Naturally, she couldn't hear their voices above the confusion.

Now the *Lurline* began smoothly to slip away from its berth, and as Jane and Mrs. Hope blew more kisses and waved more goodbyes, the water below began to widen between them and the dock.

Still, Jane noted, her young friends stood with their shoulders braced, their eyes tensely, expectantly transfixed upon her, laughing and gesturing as if waiting for her to do something besides wave. But what else could she do?

Curious she looked around and then behind her, at the very moment Mrs. Hope laughed, "I *told* you I had a secret!"

For there, not two feet away, a little behind the crowd, stood August Ernst, hatless, his eyes looking as impish as when he had asked her to promise she would go. And then, right before all of her friends he took a quick step, spread his arms wide, encircled Jane and kissed her tenderly.

While Mrs. Hope hurried off to look for Rhett, Jane and Mr. Ernst, there with their arms around each other, took up their post together and started waving.

Now Al and Wally together let out such a holler that this time Jane could hear them.